Circuit weigh

A STEP-BY-STEP FITNESS PLAN

Circuit weight training

EFFECTIVE, FLEXIBLE TRAINING PLANS FOR FITNESS, HEALTH, STRENGTH AND STAMINA

by

TONY LYCHOLAT

THORSONS PUBLISHING GROUP

First published 1989

© TONY LYCHOLAT 1989

British Library Cataloguing in Publication Data

Lycholat, Tony
Circuit weight training.
1. Weight training
I. Title
796.4'1

ISBN 0-7225-1868-4

Published by Thorsons Publishers Limited, Wellingborough,
Northamptonshire NN8 2RQ, England

Printed in Great Britain by
Woolnough Bookbinding Limited, Irthlingborough, Northamptonshire

3 5 7 9 10 8 6 4 2

Contents

Acknowledgements   7
Introduction: the evolution of circuit weight training   9

1 Understanding fitness   13
2 Fitness assessment   17
3 Structuring your training programme   25
4 Training terms   29
5 Training programmes — general circuits   34
               — muscular endurance circuits   37
               — aerobic circuits   38
               — outdoor circuits   39
               — strength circuits   40
               — power circuits   41
               — specific circuits   43
6 Warming up   46
7 Warming up exercises (mobilisers)   48
8 Lower body exercises   61
9 Upper body exercises   72
10 Bounding exercises (plyometrics)   89
11 Warming down and stretching   100
12 Stretches (preparatory and developmental)   102

Appendix 1 Perceived exertion   122
Appendix 2 Muscle charts   123

References   126

For Deborah, who put up with so much.
My love, always.

Acknowledgements

In common with all my previous efforts, this book was put together with the help and understanding of many people. Special thanks must go to the models featured in all the exercises, namely Karin Potisk, Sally Lee and Tim Hutchings; to *Reebok* and *Nike* for supplying clothes and footwear; to my training partner over the last couple of years, Robert Hilton, for sharing his knowledge; to friends and colleagues at Flames Health Club, particularly Chérie, whose insanity kept me sane throughout the writing of the manuscript; to Chantal and Bridget, who kept me in one piece through the bad times; and, of course, to Flo, whose tea fuelled every word. Thanks.

Introduction: The evolution of circuit weight training

Put simply, Circuit Weight Training (CWT) is a form of physical conditioning which entails moving from one weight training exercise to another in succession. When you have completed all your designated exercises in the appropriate order, you have done one 'circuit'. You then have the option of continuing the training session by completing more circuits.

Naturally, this is a vast oversimplification of this method of training and does little to explain its current popularity. Circuit Weight Training's rise to become one of the most favoured methods of exercising currently available is perhaps best explained with a look at its evolution.

As you might imagine, CWT has evolved from circuit training. Whilst it could be argued that some form of circuit training has been practised since the earliest days of physical education, it was not until the early 1960s that circuit training gained its title, a specific structure and its widespread acceptance as a highly efficient and effective form of training.

This was largely due to the publication of the first comprehensive book on the subject. Called simply *Circuit Training*, it was written by two physical education lecturers, R.E. Morgan and G.T. Adamson, based at Carnegie College, Leeds, England. As the story goes, they had both been looking for a method of keeping sportsmen and women generally fit during the non-competitive phases of the athletes' year. They hit upon circuit training and their book represented their combined extensive practical and theoretical experience of this method of physical conditioning.

Circuit training effectively passed into the physical education curriculum of virtually every school in the British Isles. In its early form, and the way most people remember it from their schooldays, a typical circuit training session went like this:

A series of exercises for different body parts were arranged in the school hall or gym. Some exercises involved benches, some used medicine balls, some used the ropes and wallbars whilst others were free-standing and used your own body weight, or some times the weight of a partner. Upon the whistle signal from your P.E. teacher, you started on your first exercise. After a designated period of time, often 30 seconds, the whistle was blown and you moved swiftly on to the next exercise, with everyone in the group moving round in the same direction. Upon the next whistle, you started the next exercise. The sequence continued in this fashion until all the exercises in the circuit had been completed. Depending now upon the fitness of the class, or more often the whims of your teacher, you were given a short recovery period of a few minutes only before being required to repeat the circuit of exercises again, usually up to three times.

There were several variations on this theme. For instance, some circuit training programmes were organized such that a number of weeks' training was preceeded by an 'assessment session' during which you established just how many repetitions of each exercise you could do in a given time period, such as one minute. You then, commonly, did half this number of repetitions at each exercise station. Some circuits also catered for different levels of fitness via simple colour-coding methods. So, for example, fitter people would do 20 repetitions (red code) of a certain exercise; less fit people would 15 repetitions (green code) of the same exercise. Both these methods obviously assessed one's level of improvement. In the first example, a reassessment after a few weeks training would indicate the level of improvement in terms of how many more repetitions of each exercise you could now do compared to when you started. In the second example, the effect of regular circuit training would be to enable you to move 'up' a code as fitness developed.

Whatever method was used, however, circuit training produced results in a remarkably short time, and large numbers of people could train all at the same time independently not only of their fitness level, but also their starting time, joining in at an appropriate exercise as they

arrived. Small wonder then, that circuit training took off in a big way with sports coaches and school teachers.

Since these early days, circuit training has been modified and adapted in countless ways, invariably proving its worth in many areas of sport and fitness. There are circuits to improve explosive power, circuits designed to improve strength and endurance, circuits which emphasize aerobic fitness and circuits with a deliberate upper- or lower-body bias. Most circuits have involved simple equipment at most, more recent developments have incorporated free weights and sophisticated resistance training machines. Such methods, involving weights other than body weight, have thus come to be called Circuit Weight Training (CWT).

Weight training has been shown to improve many components of fitness according to how the programme is put together: CWT adds a further dimension to this. Essentially, weights introduce yet another variable into all the factors which can be manipulated in order to get the appropriate or desired training effect. Depending upon the choice of exercises, their intensity and duration and the nature of the recovery between exercises, virtually any component of fitness you choose can be enhanced. CWT also allows a massive amount of work to be carried out in a relatively short time, which lends itself to quite dramatic improvements in fitness levels. It is this last point which has led to the popularity of CWT, particularly over the last couple of years, with the general public. CWT is seen as a valid and effective choice when it comes to a method of exercising which can enhance all components of fitness and achieve a balance between upper and lower body conditioning, since it is possible to design a 'total fitness' circuit.

Research studies which have looked at the physiological benefits of CWT have shown quite significant improvements in muscular strength, endurance and power. With appropriate stretching exercises forming part of the warm up and cool down phases of each CWT session, the component of flexibility can also be improved. Some studies, though not all, have even shown quite dramatic improvements in aerobic fitness as a result of CWT, though this, as with all components of fitness, really depends upon how your circuit is put together. However, it has to be agreed that it is possible to design a 'total fitness' circuit for general health and fitness benefits lasting no longer than 45 minutes: and it is this type of circuit which has taken off in a big way in health clubs in the last few years.

Essentially, this book aims to show you how to put together CWT programmes to emphasize different components of fitness. Some of these programmes require sophisticated equipment, some of them require no equipment at all, other than your own body weight. Sportsmen and women will find ideas and programmes which will be of use to them whatever their sport just as the recreational exerciser will find new and interesting methods of both maintaining and improving fitness levels. If you are aiming to complement your existing training through CWT, or looking to substitute that training with CWT, how you go about this is clearly explained. In fact, this book has been written in such a way that everybody interested in exercise and training, at whatever level, can find something of value within these pages.

1
Understanding fitness

In order to put together a circuit weight training programme that is appropriate for you, there are several questions that you must first ask yourself. Perhaps the most important of these questions is 'what am I trying to achieve?' Essentially, you need to determine exactly *why* you intend to follow a CWT programme, or any exercise programme for that matter.

To help you answer this question, it is worthwhile considering the nature of fitness and why improvements in certain components of fitness can be useful in terms of your health, fitness or sports performance.

Being physically fit means that you can cope with whatever demands life throws at you, including the unexpected.

Fitness is both specific and relative. It is specific since the benefits you get from a training programme largely depend upon who you are, the type of exercise you do and how you do it. Fitness is relative since there are levels of fitness: a recreational exerciser will be fitter generally speaking than the sedentary office worker, yet the Olympic athlete is fitter than both.

In order to better understand the concept of fitness, sports scientists have analysed physical fitness and expressed it in terms of its component parts. These have been placed in one of two groups, either 'health-related' or 'skill-related'.

The health-related components are so-called since it is thought that an improvement in any or all of them leads to an improvement in the general health and well-being of the individual. The skill-related components are so-called since they are directly linked to the performance of activities, both in everyday life and in the sporting arena.

Obviously, there is considerable overlap between the groupings. Some activities require a high level of skill before many of the health-related components of fitness can be developed: the game of tennis is just one such example. To sustain a rally requires a certain skill level in the first instance. The novice may well find himself developing racquet skills and ball control long before his practice sessions enhance his cardio-respiratory endurance to any great extent.

A person can be deemed generally fit if they have a good balance of all components of fitness. Few activities, if any, promote *all* components of fitness, hence the popularity of mixing and matching fitness activities, with one complementing the deficiencies in the other. Many distance runners, for instance, balance out their essentially aerobic training with weight training and exercises for the upper body, usually, it must be said, in the form of circuit weight training.

COMPONENTS OF PHYSICAL FITNESS
AND THEIR DEFINITIONS

Physical fitness
{
'Health-related' fitness
{
Cardio-respiratory endurance
Muscular endurance
Muscular strength
Flexibility
Body composition
}

'Skill-related' fitness
{
Agility
Balance
Co-ordination
Speed
Power
Reaction time
}

HEALTH-RELATED COMPONENTS

● **Cardio-respiratory endurance (efficiency):** a measure of how good your body is at supplying fuel for physical activity and at dispersing those products which cause fatigue.

● **Muscular endurance:** a term which reflects the ability of a muscle or muscle group to repeatedly perform exercise in the absence of fatigue.

● **Muscular strength:** a term which reflects the ability of a muscle or muscle group to exert maximum force.

● **Flexibility:** a measure of the range of movement at a joint or joints.

● **Body composition:** a term which relates the amount of fat tissue which a body has to the amount of lean tissue (bone, muscle, etc.).

SKILL-RELATED COMPONENTS

● **Agility:** a measure of the ability to rapidly change the position of the whole body in space, quickly and accurately.

● **Balance:** a measure of the ability to maintain equilibrium whilst either stationary or moving.

● **Co-ordination:** a measure of how effectively the senses can be used together with body parts to effect movements and tasks smoothly and accurately.

● **Speed:** a measure of how quickly a movement can be performed.

● **Power:** a measure of the rate of doing work.

● **Reaction time:** a measure of the time taken to respond to a stimulus.

COMPONENTS OF FITNESS — WHO NEEDS WHAT?

Different benefits are associated with the different components of fitness. Below are listed the major benefits associated with each fitness component.

FITNESS COMPONENT

BENEFITS

● **Cardio-respiratory endurance (CRE):**

An improvement in this component of fitness has been linked to a decrease in a person's risk of heart disease. Exercise programmes which emphasize this aspect of fitness have also been used very successfully in the management of obesity and adult-onset diabetes. The development of a high level of CRE is a prerequistite for successful participation in most sports and is a necessary foundation for other components of fitness.

● **Muscular endurance:**

Possessing muscular endurance allows for the efficient repetition of tasks in everyday life and movements in sport. Muscular endurance is essential for good posture. Muscular endurance, in combination with CRE is often referred to as 'aerobic fitness'.

● **Muscular strength:**

A high level of muscular strength allows you to lift, carry and move objects, including yourself, with relative ease. Strength is also necessary for good posture, and strong muscles help to stabilize and protect joints against injury.

● **Flexibility:**

Being flexible allows you to reach, bend and twist with ease. Flexibility is essential for good posture and also allows you to take full advantage of your movement potential, allowing you to exert force through the widest range possible — which is essential for all sports. A high level of flexibility has also been linked to a reduction in exercise and sports-related injuries.

● **Body composition:**

The correct balance between fat and lean tissue is vital to health and sports performance. Being overfat can lead to ill-health and will almost certainly slow down the sports performer.

● **Skill-related:**

All are necessary to a greater or lesser extent during sports and exercise activities, according to the level of participation and the activity in question. Each component is best enhanced in drills which mimic the way the skill will be performed during the sport or exercise itself. Having said that, all these components will be improved during some of the circuits outlined, particularly during the power circuits.

[A more detailed breakdown of the components of fitness, specifically those that are health-related, is given in *Shape Your Body, Shape Your Life* (Patrick Stephens Limited, £3.99).]

Having outlined the benefits associated with different components of fitness, you probably have a good idea about which components of fitness you may want to enhance. The next stage in designing your circuit training programme is to gauge your current fitness level.

The following section provides a number of simple fitness tests which will help to determine your starting point. Repeated on a regular basis, such tests will also enable you to monitor your improvement.

2

Fitness assessment

Just as physical fitness has a number of components, so several tests need to be carried out in order to give an overall picture of your current fitness level.

Obviously, there are some extremely elaborate (and expensive) tests which can be done to gauge your fitness levels. Most people do not have access to the equipment nor the expertise which is necessary for such tests, hence the battery of tests which is given here features the simplest tests of fitness which are at the same time accurate enough to estimate your starting point and any improvement you will make if you train on a regular basis. Before you begin your fitness assessment though, you need to ask the following question:

ARE YOU FIT TO EXERCISE?

This may seem like a foolish question, but research has shown that people who fall foul of injury — or worse — during exercise should not have been exercising in the first place. Whilst it is true that virtually everyone can begin a well-designed exercise programme immediately with no problem, there are some exceptions to this rule when extra care and specialist advice are necessary. Consult your GP and/or an exercise specialist or training adviser if you can answer 'yes' to any of the following questions in this simple questionnaire.

PRE-EXERCISE QUESTIONNAIRE

	YES	NO
1) Has your doctor ever told you that you have high blood-pressure or any cardiovascular problem?	☐	☐
2) Is there any history of heart disease in your family?	☐	☐
3) Have you ever been troubled by unaccountable chest pains or tightness in the chest, especially if associated with minimal effort?	☐	☐
4) Are you prone to headaches, fainting or dizziness?	☐	☐
5) Have you any medical condition which you think might interfere with your participation in an exercise programme?	☐	☐

6) Do you suffer from pain or limited movement in any joint? □ □

7) Are you taking any drugs or medications at the moment? □ □

8) Are you extremely overweight or extremely underweight? □ □

9) Are you a newcomer to exercise and over 40 years of age? □ □

10) Are you pregnant? □ □

Even if you can answer 'no' to all of these questions, do progress steadily through the circuit training programme that you decide to follow, especially if you have been physically inactive for some time. Remember at all times to listen to your body before, during and after your exercise/training session.

BEFORE EXERCISE

Do not exercise at all if you feel even slightly unwell or if you have a virus. Similarly do not exercise without specialist advice if you have an injury of any sort, and never exercise after a heavy meal or after drinking alcoholic beverages.

DURING EXERCISE

Whilst you are exercising, avoid unnecessary exertion. Dizziness, nausea, mental confusion, rapid or irregular breathing, skin pallor and unsteadiness are all obvious bodily signs of over-exertion. Decrease the intensity of exercise immediately. Consult specialist advice where necessary. Always listen to sensations of pain — there is a difference between the sensation of working hard and that sensation associated with damaged tissues. Untoward and sudden pain is invariably a sign that damage is occurring to muscles, joints or bones. Stop exercising immediately and again consult specialist advice.

AFTER EXERCISE

Extreme soreness or tenderness following exercise, especially if it is two days after the exercise or training bout indicates that the training session was too intense. Cut back on the intensity and duration of the session next time and/or check that you warmed up and warmed down thoroughly.

ASSESSING CARDIO-RESPIRATORY ENDURANCE

Whilst there are numerous methods of assessing cardio-respiratory endurance and aerobic fitness, one of the simplest is based upon the '12-minute run test' originally designed by Dr Kenneth Cooper, one of the men who was undoubtedly responsible for the running and exercise craze in America during the 1960s. The version outlined here is known as the 'one-and-a-half mile run test'

and is particularly simple to administer. (The 12-minute test and scoring tables are given in *Shape Your Body, Shape Your Life*.) Like all running tests, it suffers from the fact that running technique, pace judgement, weather conditions and running surface can all influence the final result, and hence the fitness rating given, but if repeated under the same 'test' conditions it is reasonably accurate. It is a particularly good test to use if running features in your chosen sport or activity to any great extent.

To carry out the test you need an accurately-measured distance of one-and-a-half miles. An athletic track is obviously particularly suitable for this test. (If another measured distance is used, even if you are not sure it is exactly the required distance, repeating the test over the same distance will at least enable you to monitor your progress, even if the score according to the table below is not necessarily correct.)

Having measured out your course and warmed up thoroughly, all you now need to do is cover the distance as quickly as possible. Make a note of the time it takes you to complete the distance, warm down thoroughly, then compare your time with the table below according to your age and sex.

Age (years)	very poor	poor	fair	good	very good	excellent	superb
Men							
17-29	16:30 +	14:30 +	12:00 +	10:15 +	8:15 +	7:30 +	6:45 +
30-34	17:00 +	15:00 +	12:30 +	10:30 +	8:30 +	7:45 +	7:00 +
35-39	17:30 +	15:30 +	13:00 +	10:45 +	8:45 +	8:00 +	7:15 +
40-44	18:00 +	16:00 +	13:30 +	11:00 +	9:00 +	8:15 +	7:30 +
45-49	18:30 +	16:30 +	14:00 +	11:15 +	9:15 +	8:30 +	7:45 +
over 50	19:00 +	17:00 +	14:30 +	11:30 +	9:30 +	8:45 +	8:00 +
Women							
17-29	19:48 +	17:24 +	14:24 +	12:18 +	9:54 +	9:00 +	8:06 +
30-34	20:24 +	18:00 +	15:00 +	12:36 +	10:12 +	9:18 +	8:24 +
35-39	21:00 +	18:36 +	15:36 +	12:54 +	10:30 +	9:36 +	8:42 +
40-44	21:36 +	19:12 +	16:12 +	13:12 +	10:48 +	9:54 +	9:00 +
45-49	22:12 +	19:48 +	16:48 +	13:30 +	11:06 +	10:30 +	9:36 +
over 50	22:48 +	20:24 +	17:24 +	13:48 +	11:24 +	10:30 +	9:36 +

ASSESSING MUSCULAR STRENGTH AND MUSCULAR ENDURANCE

Although muscular strength and endurance are two different components of fitness they are related as indicated on page 15. The timed sit-up test is an indicator of both these components of fitness and is simple to perform. This test has been used extensively in a variety of situations and is popular for reasons other than its obvious simplicity: many researchers feel that assessing the condition of the abdominal muscles is very relevant to everyday life tasks as well as in sports performance because of the important role of these muscles in posture, the prevention of back pain and in linking upper and lower body movements.

The person to be tested lies on the floor with knees bent, feet comfortably apart and arms folded across the chest. The tester holds the subject's ankles down so that both feet are kept firmly in contact with the floor at all times. Upon a signal from the tester, the subject curls up so that his or her elbows, still in close contact with the chest, touch the thighs before curling down again. As the subject's mid-back touches the floor, the movement sequence is repeated.

After 30 seconds the tester stops the test, having counted the exact number of completed curl-ups performed in this time period.

As with all abdominal exercises, it is important to breathe out as you curl up and to breathe in on the return movement. Emphasize correct technique at all times.

Typical scores for this test would be:

Rating	20-39 years	40-49 years
Poor	less than 17	less than 12
Fair	17-19	12-15
Average	20-21	16-17
Good	22-23	18-19
Excellent	24 or more	20 or more

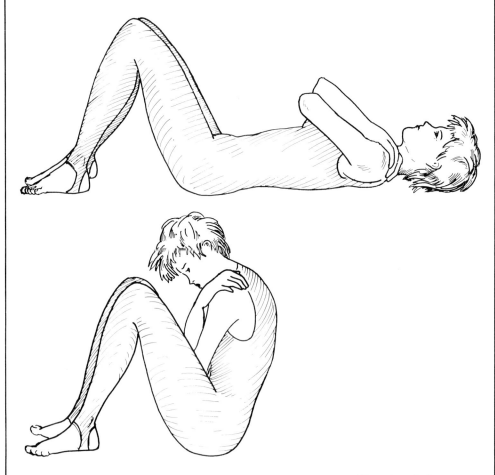

The timed sit-up test.

ASSESSING FLEXIBILITY

Although it could be argued that a variety of joints and muscles should be assessed before somebody should be deemed 'flexible', this is often time consuming. A good general test of overall flexibility is thought to be the simple 'sit-and-reach test'. Whilst this essentially measures the range of movement of the lower back and hamstring muscles, it does seem to correlate well with the range of movement found at other joints. If you do wish to compare the improvements in the range of your movements at other joints, always bear in mind that you can use any of the stretching exercises given in this book as 'tests', comparing how far you can now go in relation to when you began exercising.

For the sit-and-reach test you will need a stout box and a ruler. Place the box against the wall and tape the ruler to the box with clear tape, so that half of the ruler projects over the end of the box. Warm up thoroughly then sit in front of the box with your bare feet placed against it whilst keeping your legs straight. Reach as far forward as possible with outstretched fingers and note how far along the ruler your fingertips are. Distances past the edge of the box should be recorded as 'plus' values; distances in front of the box should be recorded as 'minus' values.

Generally speaking, minus values are poor, a zero rating (to the edge of the box) is average, whilst any plus reading is good.

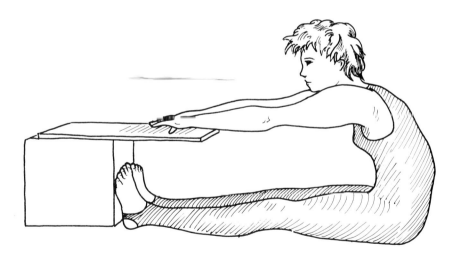

The sit-and-reach test.

ASSESSING BODY COMPOSITION

The assessment of body composition requires the use of skinfold calipers and a skilled technician. You can, however, get a good idea of how your body composition is changing by taking specific girth measurements and by assessing your physique as honestly as possible in a mirror. Remember to take all girth measurements in the same spot each time. Bear in mind too, that your weight does not tell you about your body compo-

sition, it just tells you what everything — lumped together — actually weighs. Your body composition may well change dramatically yet your weight stay the same, as you increase muscle mass and decrease fat tissue as a result of regular training.

ASSESSING EXPLOSIVE POWER

As explained on page 42 power is a prerequisite to successful participation in a wide variety of sports. A useful, yet simple, measure of explosive power is the vertical jump test.

For this test you need a high wall, a long ruler or yardstick and the help of a friend. Having warmed up, stand sideways to the wall, a few inches away from it. Reach up as high as possible with the hand nearest the wall, fingers outstretched, and have your friend note the position of your

fingertips. Now wet your fingers (or use chalk dust), crouch down and leap as high as possible to touch the wall again. Your partner should then measure the distance between the two marks you have made. The best of three attempts is usually taken.

Ideally, you also need to take into account your body weight in this test. The following table gives you a rating based upon body weight and vertical distance jumped.

DISTANCE

POWER

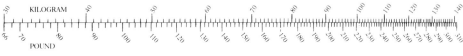

WEIGHT

This table is known as the Lewis Nomogram. To use it, lay the straight edge of a ruler linking your body weight on the right hand column to the vertical distance you managed to jump on the left hand column. The point at which the straight edge crosses the middle column gives you your power output.

ASSESSING POSTURE

Whilst not a component of fitness, good posture is vital to one's health and well-being. Not only that, emphasizing good posture during exercise and training can also prevent injury and help you get the most from your training programme.

Whilst there is no ideal posture, due to individual differences and characteristics, there are certain things for which you should look. The diagrams below indicate good posture. Use them to help evaluate your own.

Viewing from the side, note how the vertical plumb line falls down through the ear, through the shoulder joint, approximately midway through the trunk, approximately through the greater trochanter of the femur, down through the knee, ending up just forward of the lateral malleolus at the ankle joint.

From the rear, note the symmetry. The head is balanced, shoulders are level, as is the pelvis and the legs are straight. This is a good position to view the feet, since in the standing position with good posture the Achilles tendon should be vertical.

Having completed all the tests here, fill in an 'assessment' form such as that which follows. Repeat the tests after about six weeks of regular training and note the improvements.

SELF ASSESSMENT RECORD CARD

Name: _____   Age: _____   Height: _____   Weight: _____   Date: _____

Girth measurements:
Upper arm: __   Chest/bust: __   Waist: __   Hips: __   Upper thigh: __   Calf: __

Aerobic fitness (1½ mile run test) Rating: _____

Muscular endurance and strength test (timed sit-up test) Rating: _____

Flexibility (sit-and-reach test) Rating: _____

Power (vertical jump test) Rating: _____

Comments on appearance and posture: _____

_____

_____

_____

_____

3

Structuring your training programme

To achieve the maximum possible benefits from an exercise or training programme it is essential to follow some form of logical training pattern. Many athletes for instance, talk in terms of a 'training year' during which there are more or less definite phases during which certain components of fitness are emphasized. Winter, for instance, is a time when many athletes will concentrate upon building a good foundation of general fitness and strength. This phase, perhaps lasting three months, will be followed by more specific strength and power work, which in turn may be followed by speed work prior to the competitive season. Naturally, the content and structure of an athlete's year will depend upon his/her event, fitness level and any specific competitions he or she may be entering, but this 'periodization' of an athlete's year is the hallmark of all successful performers. At the highest level, Olympic athletes actually end up looking at their training programmes over a four-yearly cycle!

Whilst such a definite structure is not necessary for recreational exercisers, there are many advantages to be gained from planning your training. Certainly it helps to have goals to work towards and it makes sense to prepare your body for more strenuous work, such as the power circuits, by carrying out general foundation work like the general circuits for several weeks before you attempt them.

In view of this, it is a good idea to plan and log your training: such an approach also allows you accurately monitor your progress. A 'training diary' is the obvious way to do this. Start it off with your fitness assessment record sheet on page 24. Your next page should then be a general statement regarding what you intend to achieve over the next few weeks of training. This could be something as definite as wanting to lose weight, or improve explosive power, or something more general such as wanting to feel fitter. Whatever your aim, write it down. Then log each day's training as you do it. A typical record card is given at the end of this section, along with an explanation of how to fill it in. Use your record card not only to write down your training, but also to help you gauge how your training might be modified the next week. If one exercise is particularly easy, comment upon this in the 'comments' section and change it accordingly next time you train.

At the end of several weeks' training, perhaps twelve, reassess your fitness level and insert another assessment sheet into your training log. Using this, and your feelings about how your training has gone in the preceeding weeks, develop and modify your training programme for the coming months according to whether your goal has or has not been achieved, or if you now have a new training aim. Repeat the process on a regular basis: three months is usually appropriate. Should you ever wonder whether your training is worth it, go back to the first page in your training log and compare it to the last page — you'll be amazed at the difference!

Just as it is important to have a training aim and a logical training pattern over a period of months, it is equally important to structure your week by week training and indeed each training session itself.

On a weekly basis, you should make sure that you train often enough for training benefits to occur as indicated in the specific circuits section — you should also make sure that you get sufficient rest and recovery periods between exercise bouts: this information is also given in the relevant circuits section.

As far as each session goes, you should always warm up thoroughly, work through the appropriate circuits following good exercise technique at all times and warm down thoroughly at the end of the session. (See Chapters 6, 7 and 11 on warming up, warming down and stretching.)

RECORD CARDS

This is an example of the type of record card you might like to use to record your training.

The top line is self explanatory. Fill in here the session number (whether the first, second, third, etc, of the week). Indicate in the 'week number' space whether you are in your fourth week of training, or whatever. You may like to start each new training phase at week 'one'. Obviously, fill in the date.

The far left column allows you to write down the exercise you are doing and the recovery. If your recovery is rest, then there is no need to enter anything in the 'R' line. However, if it is active and involves cycling, jogging, etc., log this down in the appropriate space.

The second column allows you to note down the weight that you are using on any of the exercises. The third column is for the number of repetitions of an exercise. If you are doing your circuit according to time, you might still like to count the number of repetitions you are doing and log them during your recovery time.

The 'time' column is there to note down the time spent exercising. You may like to add up the total time spent exercising (or recovering) in each circuit for further comparison of training methods.

The final column allows you to multiply the number of repetitions of an exercise by the weight you are using, to give you an idea of the total work you are doing. This column is particularly useful if you are doing strength work. There is also space to summate all the work done in terms of weight lifted in the 'total' column.

You may like to fill in this type of record card for each training session. If your sessions are essentially the same for a week or two, you need only fill in the card when you have changed your training at all.

In order to do this, make several copies of the blank record card here. A completed record card is also given by way of illustration.

Record card

Session no:	Week no:		Date:		
Exercise (E) or recovery (R)	Weight	Repetitions	Time	Workload (weight × repetitions)	
E					
R					
E					
R					
E					
R					
E					
R					
E					
R					
E					
R					
E					
R					
E					
R					
					Total

Number of circuits:
Comments:

Record card

Session no: 2	Week no: 8	Date: 05/03/88			
Exercise (E) or recovery (R)	Weight	Repetitions	Time	Workload (weight × repetitions)	
E FRONT SQUATS	50 Kg	15		750	
R	/		60 secs		
E BACK SQUATS	60 Kg	15		900	
R	/		60 secs		
E LEG EXTENSIONS	20 Kg	15		300	
R	/		60 secs		
E LEG CURLS	15 Kg	15		225	
R	/		60 secs		
E HIP EXTENSIONS	5 Kg	15		75	
R	/		60 secs		
E HYPEREXTENSIONS	/	15		/	
R	/		60 secs		
E					
R					
E					
R					
				2250 Kg per circuit	Total

Number of circuits: ×3

Comments: LOWER BODY BIAS CIRCUIT FOR STRENGTH/ENDURANCE ALTERNATE WITH UPPER BODY BIAS CIRCUIT.

4
Training terms

Whilst the various CWT programmes are different, they all use the same training terms.

Each individual exercise can be done a number of times. In one of the strength circuits for instance, you may well be directed to perform six repetitions of the bench press exercise. This series of six repetitions would then be described as one **set**. The number of repetitions and the number of sets performed upon each exercise will vary according to which component/s of fitness you are trying to enhance and your fitness level.

Exercises which involve either body weight, free weights (dumbbells and barbells) or machines are known as **resistance exercises**. The amount of resistance you are overcoming (the weight you are lifting) is often referred to as the **load**. To get some idea of the total amount of work you are doing during each exercise, it is convenient to multiply the load by the number of repetitions in each set. If you do this for each set of an exercise this allows for further comparison of your improvement. There is space on each CWT record card to do this. (Note that this is an estimate only, since no measure has been made of the distance through which you are applying force.)

It is possible to rest between exercises, or do some other form of exercise. If the recovery phase between exercises involves a different activity which aids recovery, this is known as '**active recovery**'. A period of exercise is also often known as a '**work interval**' especially if it is to be repeated. Correspondingly, the recovery period between work intervals is often referred to as the '**rest**' (or **recovery**) **interval**.

When it comes to discussing muscular contractions, a number of terms are used according to how muscles are changing length as they are developing force to overcome (or attempt to overcome) resistances.

Concentric is the term used to describe that type of contraction when a muscle shortens as it overcomes resistance. (Concentric contractions are also referred to as '**positive work**').

Static is used to describe that type of contraction when a muscle maintains its length whilst developing tension.

The term **eccentric** is used to describe that type of contraction when a muscle attempts to overcome a resistance whilst it is lengthening. (Eccentric contractions are also referred to as '**negative work**.')

Isokinetic is the term used to describe that type of contraction when muscles cause the angle at joints to change at a constant speed, or rate. Such contractions are only truly possible using sophisticated electronic equipment.

Concentric, static and eccentric contractions are features of everyday life and sport. All muscular movements will at some stage involve a combination of these types of contraction in sequence. The following diagram illustrates this point in relation to a standard weight training exercise, the squat.

As you squat down, the muscles at the front and back of your thighs and buttocks control the movement towards the floor through eccentric (lengthening) contractions. Muscles of the trunk and spine meanwhile maintain the 'long back' position through static contractions. Rising from the squat position subsequently involves the muscles at the front and back of your thighs and buttocks in concentric (shortening) contractions.

A phrase which is gaining wider and wider usage in exercise is **'training specificity'**. This refers to the fact that the body adapts to training according to the way it is trained. Training muscles through a limited range of movement seems to condition them through that range of movement only, for example. Similarly, running at slow speeds makes you better at running at slow speeds and not at any other pace. This argument can also be applied to training with weights. If your sport or recreational activity requires you to develop high forces relatively quickly then you should train in a similar fashion.

However, whilst this is generally true, it must be borne in mind that general conditioning forms the ideal base for specific training, and, as has already been pointed out, makes for a more balanced sports performer who is less susceptible to injury. A good sports conditioning programme is thus a unique blend of general and specific training.

TYPES OF EQUIPMENT

The recent and continuing popularity of weight training has led to a massive increase in the types of weight training equipment that you are likely to come across.

At the simplest level are the traditional 'free weights' such as barbells and dumbbells and a variety of wrist and ankle weights. Free weights come in a variety of materials, from plastic-encased concrete to chrome-plated iron, and vary tremendously in price. If you intend to purchase a free weights set, make you that you have enough weight discs, bars and collars to allow you to do all the exercises you want to do without having to stop after each exercise to 'break' a bar in order to use a different weight.

Some exercises may require weight stands or a bench. Again, if purchasing such items make sure that they are heavy duty and well made. Bear in mind that the more nuts and bolts required to assemble a bench the more parts there are to work loose. All steel, welded pieces of equipment manufactured from heavy-gauge box section are recommended.

It is common to find some form of multigym or single station units in many sports centres and clubs.

Essentially, such items have weight stacks which are guided along runners. Different exercises can be carried out on each exercise station and adjusting the weights on such pieces of equipment is simply a matter of moving the selector pin in the weight stack to a different position. Because this can be done so quickly, and because the weight stacks are safely out of the way of the user, multigyms, pulley units and single station exercise machines are ideally suited to circuit weight training.

You are also likely to come across more sophisticated exercise machines which are often referred to as being 'cam-based'. Such equipment has been designed to take into account the fact that a muscle can overcome more or less force according to the angle of the joint and the basic characteristics of muscle. Theoretically, this should mean that you can work muscles equally hard throughout their full range of movement. In practice, all such machines are manufactured with an average person in mind and do not take into account individual limb lengths, joint and muscle characteristics and the speed of shortening of muscles — all factors which influence how much resistance a person can over-come. However, such equipment is very comfortable and easy to use and, again, is very suitable for all forms of CWT.

Look out, too, for the new hydraulic machines now available which, instead of using weights as the resistance, rely upon the compression of a fluid, as well as those machines whose resistance is offered by electromagnetic braking. All are suitable for CWT if the manufacturers instructions are followed, particularly those regarding positioning yourself on each exercise station. You may well find it necessary to disregard certain training instructions — those relating to the speed at which exercise repetitions should be performed, for instance — for a number of the CWT programmes given in this book, however.

Generally speaking, as far as obtaining a training effect goes, if you follow the guidelines given in the relevant pro-grammes section, it does not matter whose equipment you use, since it is how you train that is important.

SAFETY GUIDELINES WHEN USING WEIGHT TRAINING EQUIPMENT

To get maximum benefit from weight training and to avoid injury remember to follow these guidelines:

ALWAYS:
- Warm up thoroughly
- Follow exercise technique instruc-tions to the letter
- Exercise from a firm stable base
- Wear suitable shoes
- Lift and lower weights to the floor with a straight back, bending at the knees
- Check any equipment you are about to use: are the collars tight? Is there an equal amount of weight on each end of the bar? Are the bench and stands stable?
- Add or remove weights from a bar when it is on the floor
- Get the help of a partner (spotter) for awkward, overhead or prone lying exercises (free weights only).
- Check the position of the selector pin in weight stack equipment — is it your weight?
- Adjust seat heights, etc, according to manufacturers' recommendations
- Keep hands and limbs away from moving parts
- Maintain control of the weight you are using, performing each exercise smoothly without jerking
- Listen to your body
- Warm down thoroughly

NEVER
- Sacrifice exercise technique just to lift heavier weights or to carry out more repetitions
- Fool around with weights or distract/ interfere with somebody who is training near you

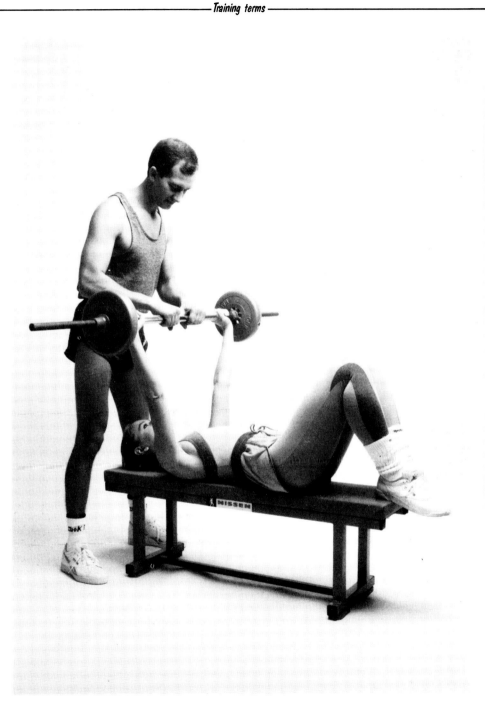

5
Training programmes

In this section you will find numerous different circuit training programmes designed to improve various components of fitness as well as programmes taking into account the presence or absence of specialist equipment. Read through them all to see which are appropriate for you.

You will note that, generally, beginners programmes are given. This is meant to show you approximately what you should be doing if you are new to this form of exercise. The exercises given are illustrative only, since the exercises you choose are up to you. The way in which they are put together is important, though, and you should use the sample circuits as a model.

No weights are given in the circuits which involve weight training apparatus. This is because people's fitness levels differ tremendously. Where an exercise has to be carried out for, say, 30 seconds, you should choose a weight which you can handle comfortably for this period of time.

Similarly, with the strength circuits, you will see that the instructions involve using a weight with which you can only do the appropriate exercise 6-8 times.

Naturally, there has to be a little bit of trial and error involved in your initial circuit training. After one or two sessions you will have managed to sort everything out.

Similarly, if you can manage one circuit when a programme recommends two, do not despair. Work steadily through the given guidelines and add exercises as the weeks go by until you are performing two complete circuits. Remember that everyone has a different starting point.

The different circuits also show you the many ways in which the amount of exercise you are doing can be increased. Even if you are not going to do all of the circuits given here, reading through them all will give you a clearer understanding of how to adapt training patterns to get the required and desired effects.

USING THE CIRCUITS IN GROUPS

The circuits given here can be used in several ways. If training on your own, then you can just proceed with which ever circuit you use. Groups of people can also use the circuits with a little forethought.

For circuits which involve rest recovery periods, exercisers can station themselves at each exercise, moving round in the same direction upon completion of that exercise. This is especially useful when working on a time basis, although not so useful when a number of repetitions are being carried out, since people do tend to complete exercises at different rates.

If no elaborate equipment is being used, then it is possible to have more than one person at each exercise station all working together and moving in the same direction. Again, this works best on a timed basis.

The active recovery circuits pose a problem when equipment such as exercise bikes is being used, since there must be as many bikes as exercisers for this method to work, if the exercise time differs from recovery time.

Repetition based circuits and the power circuits which involve covering distance can be arranged in the form of relays and competitions, as indicated in the Power Circuits section.

GENERAL CIRCUIT (EQUIPMENT BASED)

Perhaps the most popular, a general circuit is just that: it is designed to enhance as many components of fitness as possible and work both upper and lower body equally. Whilst such circuits have been shown to produce significant gains in all aspects of fitness, do bear in mind that the improvement noted in aerobic fitness with such a circuit is usually quite small, often only around 5 per cent over a ten week period. It is probably a good circuit to use as part of your foundation training for other sports or activities, and is also a good complement for activities like running, for example, which neglect other components of fitness.

This beginner's general circuit can be made progressively harder, initially, by adding another complete circuit to the training phase. When this feels comfort-

Sample beginner's general circuit

Warm up
- Mobilizers 1-8
- Preparatory stretches 1, 2, 3, 4, 5, 9, 11, 13, 15
- 5 minutes easy jogging or cycling

Training phase
- Front squats
- Bench press
- Leg curl
- Pull-ups
- Leg extension
- Arm curl
- Step on bench
- Lateral raises
- Abdominal curl
- Hyperextensions

Do each exercise with a relatively light weight, such that you can perform the exercise comfortably for 30 seconds, maintaining correct technique. Give yourself 30 seconds rest-recovery between exercises (keep upright and moving between exercises — do not sit down). Repeat the circuit twice to begin with.

Warm down
- 5 minutes easy jogging or cycling
- Stretches as before, holding each stretch for 30 seconds

able, increase the weights on the exercises slightly. As this gets easier, you can also start to cut down your recovery time, although too short a recovery does lead to very rapid and accumulating fatigue which in turn leads to poor exercise performance. Depending upon fitness, 15 seconds is about as short a recovery period as possible for this type of circuit. However you progress your circuit as the weeks go by, make sure it is steady and systematic and not asking for too much too soon from your body. This type of general circuit

should be performed 3-4 times a week on alternate days for best results. Record your progress by logging the exercises, weights and repetitions on the appropriate record card.

Obviously, this is a sample programme only — you can choose any exercises you like, although it is best to alternate upper and lower body exercises in the above fashion, incorporating exercises for all major muscle groups. Ten exercises should be sufficient, although you may want to have as many as sixteen.

GENERAL CIRCUIT (NO SPECIALIST EQUIPMENT)

You can carry out a general circuit following the rules outlined for the previous General Circuit, even if you do not have access to

specialist equipment. This type of circuit can be done in the home or in a hotel if you are away on business or on holiday.

Sample Beginner's Circuit

Warm up
● Mobilizers 1-8
● Preparatory stretches 1, 2, 3, 4, 5, 9, 11, 13, 15
● 5 minutes easy jogging on spot

Training phase
● Single leg squat
● Press ups
● Step on bench (no weights)
● Bench dips
● Squat thrusts (single leg)
● Curl ups
● Hyperextensions (lying on floor)
● Curl ups (diagonal)

As before, carry out each exercise with

good technique for 30 seconds, giving yourself 30 seconds rest-recovery between exercises. Repeat the circuit twice to begin with, progressing the workload as indicated for the previous general circuit. Obviously the purchase of even a small pair of light dumbbells gives you more exercise variety, particularly for upper body work.

Warm down
● Mobilizers 1-8, or 5 minutes easy jogging on the spot followed by the stretches as before, holding each stretch for 30 seconds

Repeat the training session 3-4 times a week at equally spaced intervals for best results.

MUSCULAR ENDURANCE CIRCUITS

A general circuit also forms the framework for many other circuits, such as a muscular endurance circuit. By the very nature of this component of fitness, the type of work involved must be prolonged. It is common, therefore, to carry out each exercise for upwards of 30 seconds, usually up to one minute. This is followed by a short rest-recovery, often as little as 15 seconds, before moving on to the next exercise in the circuit which should be for a completely different muscle group from the preceding exercise. If the circuit is general, it should involve exercises for all the major muscle groups. However, such circuits can be made more specific and may be designed to work on certain muscle groups or body parts only by employing only a few specific exercises.

Such 'biased' circuits are good complementary circuits for exercisers whose current activity programme is lacking in, for example, upper body work. Some sports coaches also advocate specific circuits based upon the analysis of a performer's activity during a game. So, if your sport requires you to work moderately hard for, say, 90 seconds, after which time you have time to recover, you could indeed design a circuit in which the work periods involving the relative muscles groups pertinent to your activity exercise for 90 seconds. These are just a few of the many options of circuit training. The same arguments can obviously also be applied to other circuits, like the strength circuits for instance.

Beginner's sample general muscular endurance circuit

Warm up
- Mobilizers 1-8
- Preparatory stretches 1, 2, 3, 4, 5, 9, 11, 13, 15
- 5 minutes easy jogging or cycling

Training phase
- Leg press
- Bench press
- Leg curl
- Upright rowing
- Front squats
- Seated press behind neck
- Leg extensions
- Pull ups
- Curl ups
- Hyperextensions

Perform each exercise for 45 seconds, maintaining good exercise technique. Rest-recovery is 15 seconds between exercises. Repeat the circuit twice to begin with.

Warm down
- 5 minutes easy jogging or cycling
- Stretches as before, holding each stretch for 30 seconds

Repeat the training session 3-4 times a week at equally spaced intervals.

Sample Lower Body Bias Endurance Circuit

Warm up
- as before

Training phase
- Leg press
- Leg curl
- Leg extension
- Hip extensions

- Lunge

Perform each exercise for 45 seconds. Rest-recovery is 15 seconds. Because this circuit is so specific, beginners should only do one circuit initially, increasing gradually to three circuits as fitness progresses.

Warm down
- as before

Sample Upper Body Bias Endurance Circuit

Warm up
- as before

Training phase
- Bench press
- Pull downs
- Seated press
- Arm curl

- Upright rowing

Perform each exercise for 45 seconds. Rest-recovery is 15 seconds. As for the previous circuit, do only one circuit initially, increasing gradually to three circuits as fitness progresses.

Warm down
- as before

It is best to do this circuit and others like it in conjunction with other circuits, such as the general circuit, or with other forms of physical activity. As part of a general training programme for example, repeat twice a week.

Naturally, the choice of exercises depends largely upon why you are exercising and is at your discretion.

AEROBIC CIRCUITS

Having said that a general circuit does little for aerobic fitness when compared to other, more traditional forms of aerobic exercise, like running, cycling and swimming, circuits *can* be designed to throw greater emphasis upon this component of fitness. So far, all the circuits described have involved rest-recovery between exercises. By changing the recovery period into active, typically aerobic activity, the aerobic demands of circuit training can be greatly improved. The aerobic effects may never be as high as those associated with a running programme (usually of the order of 25 per cent) but instances of a 10 per cent improvement of aerobic fitness have been observed with a circuit designed in the following way:

Warm up
- Mobilizers 1-8
- Preparatory stretches 1, 2, 3, 4, 5, 9, 11, 13, 15
- 5 minutes easy jogging or cycling

Training phase
- Front squats
- Easy cycling
- Bench press
- Easy cycling
- Leg curls
- Easy cycling
- Pull ups
- Easy cycling
- Leg extensions
- Easy cycling
- Arm curls
- Easy cycling
- Step on bench
- Easy cycling
- Lateral raises
- Easy cycling
- Abdominal curls
- Easy cycling
- Hyperextensions

Perform each exercise for 30 seconds with good technique then immediately follow each exercise with 30 seconds of easy cycling. Repeat twice to begin with.

Warm down
- Mobilizers 1-8
- Stretches as before, with each stretch being held for 30 seconds.

Repeat the session 3-4 times a week at equally spaced intervals.

Essentially this circuit is a general circuit broken up with bouts of cycling. Note that any rhythmical activity can be used in place of cycling such as jogging, skipping and even squat thrusts, bench stepping and other such large muscle group activities. Choose whichever activity is most appropriate.

OUTDOOR CIRCUITS

It is also possible to extend the previous idea and structure your circuit so that it is essentially aerobic in nature. You can do this by interspersing periods of sustained running with simple exercises. Such circuits are often found in parks and woodlands, particularly in Europe, under the name of 'trim-trails'. Whilst such an ordered circuit is easy to follow, and provides exercise variety because of strategically placed items of exercise equip-ment (often made from natural items like logs), it is quite simple to structure your own. Woodlands and parks make ideal venues for such outdoor circuits, but a playing field, piece of open grassland, an athletics track or even the beach can be used according to the circumstances.

Obviously, the amount of running or jogging involved in the circuit depends upon fitness level. If you are not used to jogging, then brisk walking can be substituted until your fitness level improves. Experienced runners may even experiment with running at different speeds between exercises (*Fartlek* running) for variety. The variety offered by such a method is limited perhaps only by your imagination.

Beginner's outdoor circuit (walkers and joggers)

(This circuit assumes that the exerciser is not an experienced runner and may have to substitute periods of walking briskly for the jogging sections.)

Warm up
- Mobilizers 1-8
- Preparatory stretches 1, 2, 3, 4, 5, 9, 11, 13, 15

Training phase
- Easy jogging for 5 minutes
- 15 press ups (of appropriate level)
- Easy jogging for 2 minutes
- 30 half squats (no weights)
- Easy jogging for 2 minutes

- 15 abdominal curls
- Easy jogging for 1 minute
- Faster jogging for 30 seconds
- Easy jogging for 90 seconds
- 15 hyperextensions (lying on floor)
- Easy jogging for 2 minutes

Warm down
- Mobilizers 1-8
- Stretches as before, holding each stretch for 30 seconds

Repeat the circuit three times a week to begin with, at equally spaced intervals. Progress by extending the time spent running, adding more repetitions to each exercise, or adding more exercises.

As you can see from this circuit, it is not necessary to carry out all your circuit training based upon exercises performed for a given time period — you can decide to perform a number of exercises instead. For general fitness, 15 repetitions is usually a good number to aim for. If, as you are running, you come across small logs, use these for exercises like the arm curl, or

overhead press, etc. Be inventive!

Experienced runners should use exactly the same ideas, and may be interested to hear that the great middle distance runner, Jim Ryan, used a form of CWT in his Olympic training. Basically, he used to have simple weight training equipment at the trackside which he would use during the recovery phase of interval training. Whilst such a form of training is not generally advocated, it has its uses as part of a comprehensive training programme, for interest, variety and different training benefits.

STRENGTH CIRCUITS

Circuit training can also be used very effectively to promote strength. Yet, because strength training programmes of

any sort subject the muscles and joints to very high forces, it is best to carry out a general circuit, aerobic circuit, outdoor circuit, endurance circuit or a combination of these for a few weeks (4-6) before working specifically on muscular strength. As with the endurance circuits, you can structure a strength circuit with the whole body in mind, or structure circuits for specific parts of the body. The key to any strength circuit is to make it very demanding over a relatively short period of time, and to carry out a large volume of work. With such aims in mind, it is best to opt for a number of repetitions for each exercise, rather than exercising for a specific time period.

Beginner's sample strength circuit

Warm up
- Mobilizers 1-8
- Preparatory stretches 1, 2, 3, 4, 5, 9, 11, 13, 15
- 5 minutes easy cycling or jogging

Training phase
- Front squats
- Bench press
- Leg curl
- Pull ups
- Leg extension
- Arm curl
- Step on bench
- Lateral raises
- Abdominal curl
- Hyperextension

Perform 6-8 repetitions of each exercise, allowing 30 seconds rest-recovery between exercises. The weights you are using should be heavy enough such that you can only perform 6-8 repetitions. If you can do more, the weight is too light. Increase the weight as this occurs with your increasing strength levels. Perform 4 circuits.

Warm down
- 5 minutes easy cycling or jogging
- Stretches as before, holding each stretch 30 seconds

Repeat the session on alternate days for best results.

As you can see, the exercises used here are exactly the same as those used for the general circuit. If we wanted to work upon some specific part of the body we could structure the circuit accordingly. The lower body bias endurance circuit exercises could be used, in the manner as indicated above, to promote muscular strength of the lower body, for example. Using the same principles, we could then structure an upper body bias strength circuit if we so wished.

POWER CIRCUITS

Many people tend to confuse strength with power. Strength, as indicated earlier, refers to how much force you can produce in overcoming a resistance, such as lifting a heavy weight. Power, however, reflects not only how much force is being produced, but also how rapidly this force is being generated. In other words, it is a marriage of strength and speed. In all sports and athletics events, those performers who can develop considerable power, all other things being equal, are almost guaranteed success. Short, explosive sprints on the games field, throwing implements such as cricket balls, discus and javelin, rapid movements on the squash, tennis or badminton court, jumping vertically or horizontally — all these activities require power.

Whilst people who exhibit a high power output generally have the right physiological make-up in the first instance (in common with so many other components of fitness), power output can be increased significantly with the right type of training. The characteristic of power training is the rapid developmment of high forces. Obviously, this puts tremendous stresses upon the bones, muscles and joints. Any form of power training must therefore be laid upon a firm foundation of several weeks of strength training which, in turn, should have been preceeded by several weeks of general training.

Weight training can be used very successfully to improve power, yet perhaps the most effective form of power training, specifically for the lower body, involves only your own body weight in a variety of jumping and leaping activities. Collectively, such activities are referred to as 'plyometrics', although you may see the hopping, leaping and jumping exercises referred to as 'bounding', with those exercises which involve jumping off benches and boxes being referred to as 'depth jumping'.

All the plyometric exercises have one thing in common, namely the exercise causes a rapid loading of a muscle or muscle group as it lengthens, prior to a forceful concentric contraction. Not only do such exercises develop and enhance neuro-muscular co-ordination, but they also take advantage of a simple reflex response involving muscles which means that concentric muscular contractions tend to be much more forceful when they immediately follow eccentric contractions.

Circuits involving plyometric exercises should be carefully structured. The warm up needs to be very thorough, and power training should not immediately follow any intensive strength or endurance work — you should be very fresh when you begin. Excessively fatigued muscles are liable to rupture upon depth jumping, for example. Initially, the number of leaps and bounds should be kept low: in the training phase, for instance, beginners should not do more than 40-50 in one session. There should be a good rest-recovery of 1-2 minutes between sets/circuits.

Whilst performing the exercises, the emphasis should be on quality, aiming for a quick transfer of force from the yielding to the explosive phase. Well-cushioned, supportive shoes are a must and a sprung floor helps prevent injury.

Follow your plyometric training phase with a thorough warm down.

This type of circuit can be progressed in many ways. Obviously, the number of repetitions of each exercise can be increased, more exercises can be included, the height of the box used for the depth jump can be increased (although it is not advisable to use a box greater than 36-inches/90cm high), and exercises can be linked together effectively cutting down recovery time.

Because such circuits involve covering

Beginner's sample power circuit

Warm up
- Mobilizers 1-8
- Preparatory stretches 1, 2, 3, 4, 5, 9, 11, 13, 15
- 5 minutes easy cycling or jogging
- Mobilizers 9-13

Training phase
- Vertical jumps × 6
- Two-footed jumps × 6
- Hops (left leg) × 4
- Hops (right leg) × 4
- Leaps × 6
- Depth jumps (24-inch/60cm box, aiming for height) × 6
- Obstacle leaps × 6

Allow 1 minute rest-recovery between each set of exercises. Perform only one circuit.

Warm down
- 5 minutes easy cycling or jogging
- Mobilizers 1-8
- Stretches as before, holding each stretch for 30 seconds

Repeat the training session twice weekly.

distance, you can also set up a bounding circuit with this in mind. This is obviously quite demanding and should be employed by fitter sportspeople only. Having warmed up thoroughly perform:

- Two-footed jumps for 50 metres
- Hops (left leg) for 25 metres
- Hops (right leg) for 25 metres
- Leaps for 50 metres
- Sprint for 50 metres

The number of times this should be repeated depends upon fitness level. The distances can be varied according to fitness level too. Warm down thoroughly.

Such circuits can also be used very effectively in groups in the form of a relay, thereby introducing a competitive element.

SPECIFIC CIRCUITS

From the preceding list of circuits, you can see that there are many ways of putting exercises together to structure the most appropriate circuit training programme for your requirements. You may also appreciate that it is not necessary to always follow the same circuit. Since you can not only modify the exercises, but you can also 'mix and match' circuits if you like. For instance, you may begin your programme with a general circuit. After a few weeks you may change this to a more demanding endur- ance or aerobic circuit. After a few more weeks, you may opt for two strength circuits a week plus one aerobic circuit per week which may be indoors or outdoors, after a few weeks of this, you may find yourself doing one aerobic circuit, one en- durance circuit, one power circuit and one strength circuit each week. The options are limitless and make this form of exercise extremely interesting and varied.

Then again, you may be using CWT to complement your existing physical activity programme. Figure C lists some common sports and fitness activities, indicating to what extent they emphasize the different components of fitness. You can use this chart in two ways. If you see that your sport or activity neglects certain components of fitness, choose a circuit to make up for its shortcomings, thereby giving yourself the opportunity of achieving total fitness. On the other hand, you may think that carrying out a circuit which emphasizes the specific components of fitness which your sport requires is also a good idea. In this case, identify your activity again and choose the appropriate circuit. It really depends why you are exercising.

It is also possible to work specific parts of the body as part of a general circuit training programme. This is possible through structuring a general circuit training programme which has more exercises for a specific body part than any other

body part. Thus the general circuit given earlier could have three or four exercises within it specifically for the abdominal muscles, for example.

Sports performers may also like to include specific exercises within any of the circuit frameworks offered here. This could be in the form of agility work like stepping in and out of car tyres, or dodging round traffic cones. It could be speed related, including short shuttle sprints. Specific skill activities can feature involving football drills for soccer players, for example, or throwing drills for javelin throwers. In fact there is very little you cannot achieve with the right choice of circuit. Hopefully, this section shows the versatility of circuit weight training. Use the information here to devise your own programme or just simply follow some of the programmes given. All that you now have to do is start exercising!

Figure C

Comparison of common sports and fitness activities

Activity	Cardio-respiratory endurance	Muscular strength	Muscular endurance	Flexibility	Power	Skill	Bias
Aerobics (classes)	***	**	***	**	*	*	Lower body
Badminton	**	**	**	**	**	***	General
Basketball	***	**	***	**	***	***	General
Cycling	****	***	***	**	***	**	Lower body
Football	***	***	***	**	**	***	Lower body
Gymnastics	**	****	****	*****	*****	*****	General
Hockey	***	***	***	**	**	***	Lower body
Jogging	****	**	***	**	*	*	Lower body
Running	****	***	***	**	**	*	Lower body
Squash	**	****	***	**	***	***	General
Swimming	****	**	****	****	***	***	General
Tennis	**	***	***	**	**	***	General
Walking	***	*	**	*	*	*	Lower body
Yoga	*	**	***	*****	*	**	General

(*Note*: this chart is a general guide only.)

6

Warming up

Prior to any form of exercise session or strenuous physical activity, you should always warm up thoroughly. A good warm up is essential for several reasons. From a physiological point of view the increase in temperature brought about during the warm up phase of an exercise session leads to several noticeable changes:

● muscles can contract and relax more fully
● nerve impulses can travel more quickly and be received more readily
● muscles, tendons and joints are less likely to be damaged once you start exercising
● the response of the heart to exercise is improved
● oxygen is made more available to the muscles for energy processes and these processes can take place more efficiently

Psychologically, too, the warm up phase of an exercise session allows you to focus your mind on the subsequent training phase as well as allowing for mental and physical rehearsal of movement techniques. During the warm up phase you should have two major aims in mind:

● to increase the temperature of the body slightly (the onset of light sweating is a good indicator of this).

● to take your muscles and joints through their current range of movement, paying specific attention to those movements which are pertinent to your subsequent activity.

There are several methods of achieving these aims, with perhaps the best and most effective being referred to as a 'dynamic warm up'. Basically, this method of warming up relies upon the fact that, when muscles perform work, they produce a substantial amount of heat. Engaging muscles in large, rhythmical movements generates large amounts of heat very quickly. This heat-generating process is obviously enhanced by wearing loose fitting layers of clothing which can trap the heat next to your body. When you are really warm, and just before the training phase proper, you can remove the outermost layers (depending also upon the temperature of your immediate environment), remembering to put these layers back on after your training session to prevent excessive cooling. Part of your warm up phase should also involve wide ranging movements for all major joints and muscle groups. Having worked generally in this way, you might then want to work more specifically, perhaps going through certain exercises at much reduced intensity, before progressing to simple stretches laying specific emphasis upon muscles and joints which will be used predominantly in the training phase. This aspect of a dynamic warm up is known as 'preparatory stretching'. Unlike stretches designed for significant improvements in range of movement, preparatory stretches need only be held for a few seconds (6-10). The same technical rules apply, however. (Refer to stretching section pages 100-101 for these.)

Most people will find that they can achieve the desired effects of a warm up in around 10 minutes. Older or more unfit people generally need longer, perhaps up to 20 minutes. Bear in mind that the environmental temperature will influence your warming up time. If it is extremely cold you may find yourself needing to spend more time getting warm, with the opposite being true in very warm conditions. You will know when you are sufficiently warm when you feel generally mobile and are lightly perspiring. On the RPE scale (page 122) you would probably record 10-11.

On the following pages there is a selection of warming up exercises. You do not necessarily have to do them all — you will find specific guidance under the appropriate circuit training programme guidelines. Stretches for the preparatory stretching phase can be found in the stretching section (pages 100-121).

Note that, for the purpose of clarity, general warming up exercises are referred to here as 'mobilizers'.

7
Warming up exercises (mobilizers)

1 Shoulder circles

Stand tall with good posture. Raise your right shoulder towards your ear, take it backwards then down again in a circular motion. Repeat 12 times with a steady rhythm. Repeat the sequence with the other shoulder.

Having performed the exercise with each shoulder, now circle both shoulders at the same time, 12 times.

Breathe comfortably throughout both exercises.

2 Arm circles

Stand tall with good posture. Raise one arm forward, lift it up and take it back in a continuous circling motion. Keep your spine long throughout. Repeat 12 times with each arm.

Having performed the exercise with each arm, repeat the sequence 12 times this time with both arms together, avoiding the tendency to arch the spine.

Breathe comfortably throughout both exercises.

3 Arm running

Stand tall with good posture, feet about hip width apart. Swing your arms loosely backwards and forwards in a 'running' movement. Repeat 24 times.

Breathe comfortably throughout the exercise.

4 Side bends

Stand tall with good posture, feet slightly wider than hip width, hands on hips. Keep your spine long and lift up and over to one side, return to centre, then lift up and over to the other side. Avoid the tendency to lean forwards or backwards.

Repeat 12 times on each side with a steady rhythm, breathing out as you bend to the side, and in as you return.

5 Trunk (waist) twists

Stand tall with good posture, feet slightly wider than shoulder width, knees bent slightly. Bring your arms up in front of you, bent at the elbow.

Keeping your spine long, turn slowly round to the side, yet still keeping your hips facing forwards.

Repeat on the other side, performing the whole sequence 12 times. Breathe easily throughout.

6 Side lunge

Stand with your legs wide apart. Bend each leg alternately so that you achieve the position as illustrated.

Make sure that the knee of the bent leg is always over the foot and pointing in the same direction throughout the whole movement (moving smoothly from side to side naturally involves changing the relative foot positions). Keep the other leg straight. Repeat 12 times on each side.

Breathe easily throughout.

7 Step on bench

Stand tall with good posture in front of a strong bench, chair or stool. Step onto the bench with one foot, straightening the leg fully so that you are standing tall on the bench. Now step down using the opposite leg.

Repeat the exercise 24 times, then change the 'lead' leg and repeat a further 24 times, maintaining a good rhythm.

Breathe comfortably throughout the exercise.

8 Half squats (free standing)

Stand tall with good posture, feet about shoulder width apart. Rest your hands either on your hips, or hold them out in front of you for balance.

From this position, bend at the knees so that your thighs end up parallel to the floor. Keep your back long throughout, looking straight ahead.

Make sure as you bend that your knees follow the same line as your toes and that you fully straighten your legs as you return to a standing position. Repeat 24 times with a smooth rhythm.

Breathe in as you descend, and out as you rise.

(If you feel unstable doing the exercise, raise your heels about 1 inch/2.5cm off the ground using a block of wood or two weight discs.)

9 Jumps

[Before doing this exercise and others like it, prepare yourself fully by walking on the spot for two minutes, using the whole of the foot in a 'pawing' motion. It is also advisable to carry out preparatory stretches for the calves such as those given on page 114.]

Stand tall with good posture, feet about hip width apart. Maintaining your upright stance, bend your knees then forcefully straighten them, pushing off through your feet so that you end up jumping a couple of inches off the floor. As you land, absorb all the force of impact by using the whole of the foot and letting your heels touch the floor and allowing your knees to bend. Make sure that your knees are pointing in the same direction as your toes throughout the movement.

Repeat 24 times. Breathe easily throughout the exercise.

10 Side to side jumps

Modify the previous exercise by taking the feet out to the side and jumping off one foot at a time.

Repeat 12 times to each side, breathing easily throughout.

11 Squat thrusts (single leg)

Assume a basic press-up position as illustrated: note that hands are under the shoulders and the spine is long.

Now bring one knee towards the chest to touch the floor underneath you, taking some of your bodyweight, then smoothly bring the opposite leg underneath you, whilst forcefully extending the bent leg.

Repeat this sequence 24 times, rapidly but smoothly, alternating your legs.

Breathe easily throughout.

12 Squat thrusts (both legs)

Modify the previous exercise by bringing both legs up to the chest in one movement, then shooting them both out together. Make sure that you go through as full a range of movement as possible.

Breathe easily throughout. Repeat 24 times.

13 Burpees

A Burpee is basically an extension of the squat thrust (both legs). It differs from the squat thrust in that, having brought the knees up under the chest, you then forcefully straighten your legs to jump off the floor, extending the body at the same time.

As you land you bend at the knees and hips, place the hands on the floor to take your bodyweight, then shoot your legs out behind you.

Repeat 12 times, breathing easily throughout the exercise.

General whole body activities

Jogging/running, stationary cycling, skipping, etc., can also be used very effectively for increasing the temperature of the body. Note that such activities do not need to be very intense — keep the activity light. The perceived exertion during this phase should be 10-12. If jogging or running, remember to use the whole of the foot in the action. Also run 'tall', pushing off the floor with your back leg. Keep your shoulders and arms relaxed.

Cycling outdoors, or indoors on a machine, is great whole body exercise, too. Remember to adjust the height of the saddle so that on the down stroke of each pedal, your legs are almost fully extended. Look for a pedalling frequency upwards of 60 revolutions per minute.

Rowing machines are another good indoor option. Use your legs as much as possible during the pulling phase and avoid the temptation to round your back.

8

Lower body exercises

Squat machine (leg press)

For the muscles of the buttocks, thighs and calves.

Adjust the seat position (how you do this varies according to the type of equipment you are using) so that the angle of your knees is approximately 90 degrees. Your feet should be flat on the footplates and your lower back and shoulders must be firmly pressed into the back support. Have your hands loosely by your sides. Strongly push both feet away from you, extending your legs as fully as possible, but do not lock out your knees. Then control the movement back to your starting position. Just as the weights are about to touch the rest of the weight stack, repeat. Breathe out as you push away and breathe in on the return movement.

Some models of leg press/squat machine allow you to work each leg independently, which is useful if you think one leg is doing most of the work.

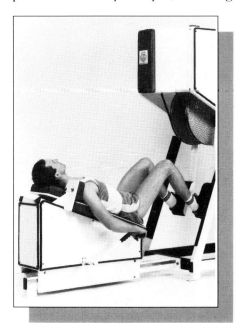 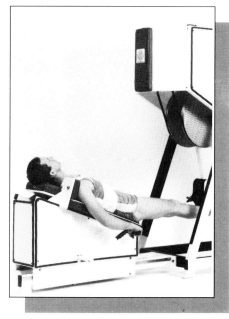

Front squats
For the muscles of the hips, buttocks, thighs and back.

This is a variation of the back squat which throws more of the training emphasis on the thigh muscles and is very applicable for runners in particular.

The technique is essentially the same as for the back squat, but the bar is rested across the front of the shoulders and maintained in that position with a 'cross-over' grip. You must keep your elbows high at all times, preferably at the same height as your shoulders. You will find that you can handle less weight than you would normally use on the back squat.

Back squats

For the muscles of the hips, buttocks, thighs and back.

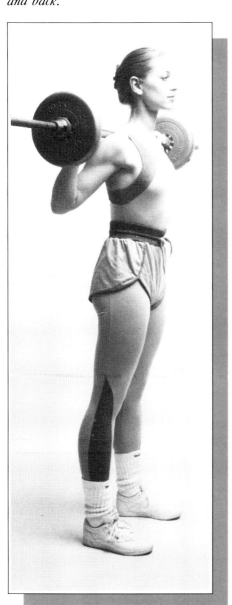

Stand tall with your feet hip/shoulder width apart. Rest a barbell comfortably across your shoulders/upper back, holding it there with a wide grip. Keeping your spine long throughout and, looking forward, smoothly bend your knees, squatting to a position in which your thighs are parallel to the floor, then strongly return to your starting position, making sure that you fully straighten your legs. Breathe in as you descend and out as your rise.

If you feel unstable because your heels are leaving the floor, stand with your heels on a block of wood (or two weight discs) approximately 1 inch/2.5cm high. Always make sure that your knees point in the same direction as your toes.

Squats (with dumbbells)

If you do not have a barbell it is possible to do a squat with two dumbbells. Rest them high on your shoulders as illustrated and carry out the exercise as indicated in the previous exercise, following the same safety instructions.

Single leg squat

For the muscles of the hips, buttocks, thighs and calves.

In the absence of any weight training equipment, this exercise can be used to condition the major muscle groups of the lower body.

Stand tall, side on to a chair or support, using it for balance. Extend your outside leg forward. Now squat down using only one leg as indicated, still keeping your spine long. Do not go any lower than a position in which your thighs are parallel to the floor. Repeat on the other leg.

Breathe in as you squat and out as you rise.

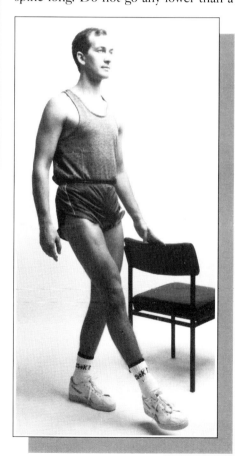

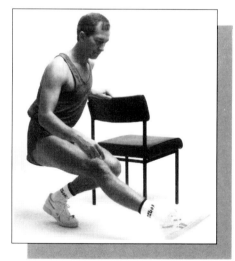

Lunge
For the muscles of the hips, buttocks, thighs and back.

Stand tall with your feet hip width apart. Rest a barbell comfortably across your shoulders/upper back, holding it there with a wide grip. Take a large step forward. Now bend your front knee, still keeping your spine long, so that your rear knee almost touches the floor. Hold this position momentarily then straighten your front leg fully. Keep your hips and feet facing forward throughout the exercise. Breathe in as you bend and out as you rise.

Repeat on the other leg.

A variation of this exercise is to step foward and bend as illustrated, but to then straighten the front leg very forcefully so that you come back to an erect standing position with both feet together again. This requires very good balance and general strength.

Both these exercises can be done holding dumbbells.

Step on bench
For the muscles of the hips, buttocks, thighs and back.

Stand tall in front of a stout, stable bench or chair with your feet approximately hip-width apart. Rest a barbell comfortably across your shoulders/upper back holding it there with a wide grip. Place one foot fully on the bench and stand upon it, bringing the other foot up beside it, then step down. Keep your back long throughout and breathe comfortably.

After stepping up the required number of repetitions with one leg, do the same number of repetitions stepping up with the other leg.

Heel raise
For the muscles of the calf.

Stand tall with a barbell resting across your shoulders/upper back maintaining it there with a wide grip. Have the balls of your feet on two weight discs or a block of wood, yet keep your heels on the floor. Now rise up onto your toes, hold your uppermost position momentarily then control the movement back to the starting position. Do not rest your heels down, instead, as soon as they touch the floor, repeat the sequence.

Keep your spine long throughout the exercise and breathe normally.

Leg (thigh) extensions
For the muscles at the front of the thigh.

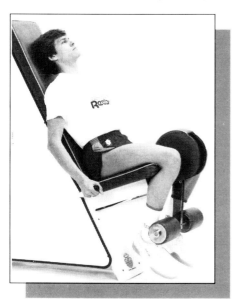

Adjust your position on the machine such that when you are seated your knees are opposite the pivot point of the machine and your whole back is pressed firmly against the back support, with your ankles behind the pads as illustrated. Loosely grasp the side handles.

Maintain this position and smoothly straighten your legs as fully as possible. Hold this position for a moment, then control the movement back to the starting position. Just before the weights touch, repeat the movement.

Breathe easily throughout the exercise.

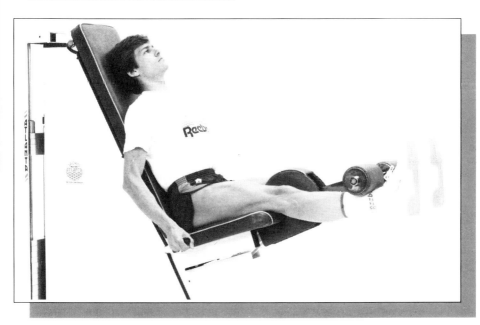

Leg (thigh) curl

For the muscles at the back of the thighs, and calves.

Lie face down on a leg curl machine with your heels under the roller pads and your knees opposite the machine's pivot point. Keep your hips pressed firmly against the bench and loosely grasp the side handles. Bend your knees, still keeping your hips pressed against the bench so that your heels come towards your buttocks.

Hold your furthermost position for a moment, then control the movement of your heels back to the starting position. Just before the weights touch the rest of the weight stack, repeat the movement.

Keep your feet flexed throughout the exercise and breathe comfortably.

Hip extensions

For the muscles of the lower back and spine, buttocks and hamstrings.

Lie face down on a box or high bench, loosely grasping its sides, such that your legs are hanging off the edge as illustrated. Keeping your legs straight and together, raise them up so that they are parallel to the floor. Hold this position momentarily, then slowly lower your legs towards the floor and repeat.

Breathe in as you raise your legs and out as you lower them.

This exercise can be made progressively more difficult by adding weights to your ankles, but do this cautiously.

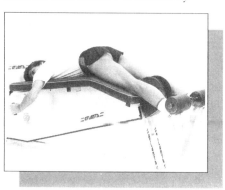

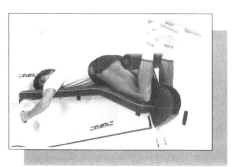

Hyperextensions

For the muscles of the back, buttocks and backs of legs.

Whilst specialist equipment has been designed for this exercise, boxes or benches of different heights can be used very effectively, as illustrated.

Place your heels under the support and position your upper body so that it is hanging down over the front bench, flexed at the hip joints, arms by sides. From this position, slowly extend the trunk so that your body comes parallel to the floor. Hold this position momentarily, then slowly lower your trunk back to the starting position and repeat.

The exercise can be made more difficult by placing your hands behind your head.

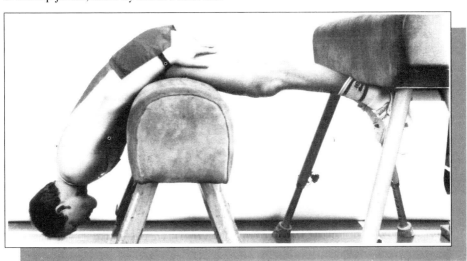

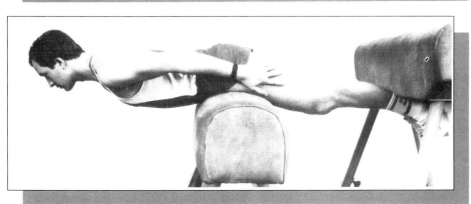

9
Upper body exercises

Bench press (press on bench)

For the muscles of the chest, front of shoulder and back of upper arm.

Lie with your back flat on a bench, making sure that your lower back is firmly pressed into the support. Hold a barbell at arms length with a wide grip above your chest (you will need the help of a partner and/or stands for this). Steadily lower the bar so that it touches the middle of your chest, then press it upwards to arms length again. Do not lock out your arms. Repeat the sequence.

Make sure that your elbows are 'under' the bar at all times and that your grip is firm, with the weight of the bar comfortably over the heel of the palm.

Breathe in as you lower the bar and out as you raise it.

Press ups

For the muscles of the chest, front of shoulder and back of upper arm.

Assume the basic starting position as illustrated. Note that the hands are underneath the shoulders and that there is a straight line from the ankles through the knees, hips and shoulders.

From this position, bend your arms so that your chest moves closer to the floor. Go as far as you can, hold your position for a moment, then straighten your arms and repeat. As you get fitter, you should aim to get to a position where your chest touches the floor. Breathe in as you lower yourself to the floor, and out on the return movement.

The exercise can be made easier by modifying the starting position and beginning the movement from your knees, and it can be made progressively harder by starting with your feet on a bench. The same technical rules apply.

Bench (chair) dips
For the muscles at the back of the upper arm, front of shoulder and chest.

Using a bench or chair for support, assume the starting position as illustrated. Now lower your bottom to the floor by bending your elbows. Just before your bottom touches the floor, hold the position, then fully straighten your arms to return to your starting position and repeat.

Breathe in as you lower and out on the return movement.

The exercise can be made easier by having the knees bent.

Dumbbell flyes

For the muscles of the chest and front of shoulders.

Lie with your back flat on a bench. Placing your feet flat on the bench helps to keep your back flat throughout the exercise. Hold a dumbbell in each hand above your chest with your elbows slightly bent. Now take your arms out to the side as far as possible, controlling the action.

Throughout the movement your hands should move in the same plane as your shoulders. Upon reaching your furthermost position, smoothly bring your arms back to the starting position.

Breathe in as you lower the weights, and out as you raise them.

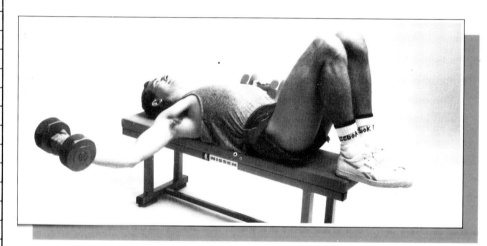

Upright rowing
For the muscles of the shoulders, upper back and front of upper arm.

Stand tall holding a barbell with an over-grasp so that your hands are approximately six inches apart with the bar at arms-length in front of you. From this position, pull the bar upwards to neck height, keeping your elbows high and the bar close to your body. Hold this uppermost position for a moment, then lower the bar under control to full arms-length again and repeat.

Breathe in as you raise the bar and out as you lower it.

Seated press behind neck

For the muscles of the shoulders, upper back and backs of the upper arms.

Sit tall on a stable bench with a bar resting comfortably across your shoulders/upper back holding it there with a wide grip. Smoothly press the barbell upwards to arms length, yet do not lock out your elbows. Return the barbell under control until it just touches the back of your neck and repeat the sequence.

Breathe in as you press the bar upwards, and out on the return movement.

Side (lateral) raise

For the muscles of the shoulder and upper back.

Stand tall with your feet approximately hip width apart, holding a dumbbell in each hand. Your arms should be slightly bent at the elbows. From this position, raise the dumbbells out to the side so that they are approximately in line with your head. Hold this position for a moment, then lower the weights under control to the starting position and repeat.

Avoid the tendency to 'throw' the dumbbells upwards and do not lean forwards or backwards as you do this exercise.

Breathe in as you raise your arms and out as you lower them.

Pull-ups

For the muscles of the upper back and front of upper arm.

A pull-up bar, pull-up frame or gymnasium beam can be used for this exercise.

Grasp the bar firmly with either an over or undergrasp (an overgrasp involves the back muscles more) and hang at full arms-length: you may have to bend your legs to do this. From this long hanging position, pull yourself up so that your head comes up past the bar.

Hold this uppermost position for a moment, then return to your starting position under control and repeat. Breathe in as you rise and out on the return movement.

The exercise can be made progressively more demanding by adding weights to the ankles.

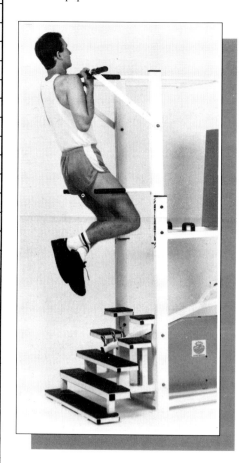
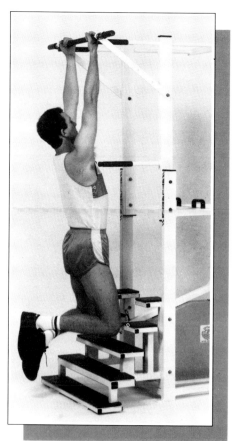

Single arm rowing
For the muscles of the upper back and those at the front of the upper arm.

Assume the position as illustrated. Note that your back should be parallel with the floor and that the dumbbell is directly below your shoulder. Smoothly bring the dumbbell to your chest, hold the uppermost position, then return the weight to arms-length again. Repeat on both sides.

Breathe in as you raise the dumbbell to the chest, and out on the return movement.

Seated tricep press
(arm extension)
For the muscles at the back of the upper arm.

Sit tall on a bench or chair. Hold a dumb-bell in one hand with your upper arm vertical, close to your head and flexed at the elbow.

From this position, straighten this arm at the elbow whilst maintaining the vertical position of the upper arm. Return the weight to the starting position under control and repeat. Perform the sequence with the other arm.

Breathe in as you raise the weight and out as you lower it.

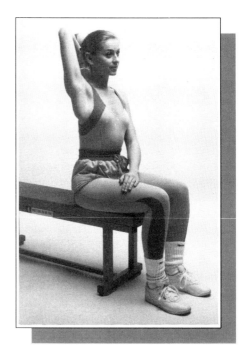

Arm (bicep) curl
For the muscles at the front of the upper arm.

Stand tall with your feet hip-shoulder width apart. Grip a barbell (undergrasp) with your hands shoulder width apart. Maintain your upright position with your arms close to your sides and smoothly bend at the elbows to raise the bar towards the chest. Return the bar to the starting position under control and repeat.

Make sure that you work through as full a range of movement as possible and avoid the tendency to lean forwards or backwards when lifting or lowering the bar.

Breathe in as you raise the bar and out as you lower it.

Alternate dumbbell curl
For the muscles at the front of the upper arm.

Stand tall, with your feet hip/shoulder width apart, grasping a dumbbell in each hand. Keeping your upper arms close to your body at all times, bend one arm at the elbow, raising the dumbbell to the shoulder, twisting the weight through 90 degrees as you do so. Return the dumbbell to the starting position under control and repeat with the other arm.

Breathe in as you raise the weights, and out as you return to the starting position.

Curl up
For the muscles at the front of the trunk.

Lie flat on the floor, knees bent at an angle of approximately 90 degrees. Rest your fingertips loosely on the side of your head, keeping your elbows back. Making sure that your lower back is pressed into the floor at all times, smoothly curl your head and shoulders up off the floor. Look upwards and ahead. The fitter you are, the higher off the floor you should curl.

Having reached your uppermost position, curl down slowly. As your shoulders touch the floor again, repeat the sequence. Breathe out as you curl up and in as you curl down.

If you curl up, twisting round to the side as you curl, you will work the side abdominals more. Remember to work both sides equally by twisting first to one side then the other.

Both these exercises can be made more demanding by working on an incline board. Bear in mind, however, that the held-down position of your feet allows the hip flexor muscles to do more of the work. On an incline board do make a conscious effort consequently to curl up and avoid the temptation to come up or down with a flat back. Do not jerk through any part of the movement.

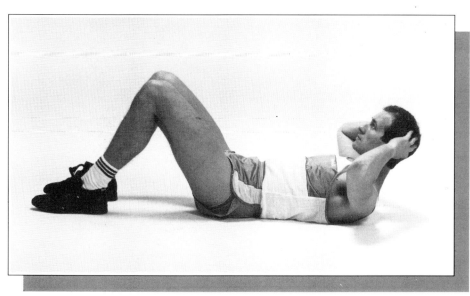

Abdominal crunch

For the muscles at the front of the trunk.

Lie flat on the floor, with your lower legs resting on a bench or chair so that your hips are directly under your knees. Rest your fingertips by the side of your head or loosely clasp your hands behind your head. From this position curl up as in the previous exercise so that your elbows touch your knees. Hold this position momentarily, then curl down under control. As your shoulders touch the floor, repeat.

Breathe out as you curl up and in on the return.

As with the previous exercise, twisting to either side as you 'crunch' works the side abdominal muscles more.

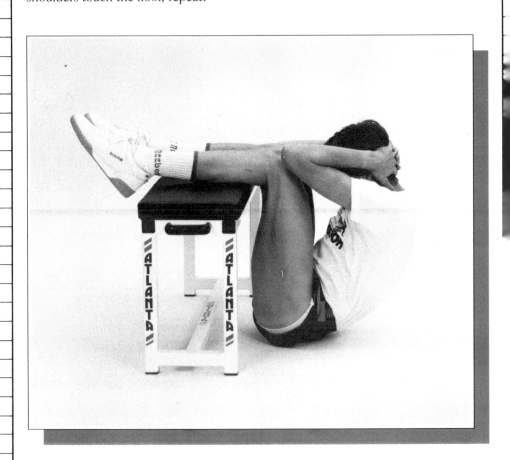

The abdominal crunch can also be done on an incline board, which increases the intensity of the basic exercise.

Abdominal machine
For the muscles at the front of the trunk.

There are many abdominal machines in health clubs and sports centres: the design and function of this model (illustrated over the page) is quite common.

Whatever the model, adjust the seat height according to the manufacturer's instructions and sit comfortably with your back pressed firmly against the support, feet hooked under the bottom rollers, loosely clasping the handles overhead.

From this position, bring your shoulders towards your hips using your abdominal muscles only, avoiding the temptation to pull excessively with your arms or feet. Curl as much as possible, hold your furthermost position momentarily, then slowly return to your starting position. Just before the weights touch the rest of the weight-stack, repeat.

Breathe out as you curl and in on the return movement.

10
Bounding exercises (plyometrics)

The following series of exercises require the ability to develop high or very high forces since they are designed to emphasize explosive power. Before doing any of them, and particularly the leaps and depth jumps, refer to the 'Power Training' section on page 41.

Vertical jumps
From an upright standing position with feet apart (one in front of the other) jump into the air. As you land, bend your hips and knees so that you can touch the floor, then explode upwards again as high as possible, changing your legs in mid air so that the rear leg is now at the front. Repeat, breathing easily throughout.

Box vault

Stand side on to a high box or bench or suitable stable object, resting both hands upon it. Jump up and over the box to land on the other side. Do one little jump to prepare yourself, then jump back over to the other side and repeat from side to side. Breathe easily throughout the exercise.

Astride bench jumps

Stand with your feet either side of a low
bench. Now jump up to place your feet
together on the bench and quickly jump
down to your starting position again and
repeat, breathing easily throughout.

Bench leaps

Stand at the end of a long bench with your feet together. Keeping your feet together, carry out small two-footed jumps, criss-crossing the length of the bench. Turn round at the end of the bench and repeat in the other direction. Breath easily throughout the exercise.

Two footed jumps

Stand tall with both feet together. From this position jump forward aiming to cover as much distance as possible. Upon landing, repeat as quickly as possible. Aim to cover the same distance with each jump. Breathe easily throughout.

Hops

Starting with either leg, hop aiming for distance as well as height. Start with little hops to begin with, then progress to large hopping movements, kicking out one leg behind you to add extra impetus to the movement. Carry out the same number of hops with both legs.

Obstacle leaps

Boxes, benches and chairs can be arranged in sequence to form an 'obstacle course'. Make sure that the obstacle heights are well within your capabilities. In this example, a light chair has been used.

Jump off two feet clearing each obstacle. If a chair is used, make sure you jump so that if your feet do strike it, the chair will fall with you (as illustrated).

2 Shoulder stretch

Stand tall with good posture. Keeping your spine long and your shoulders down away from your ears, take one arm up and behind you and take the other arm down and behind you, aiming to clasp your fingers together. You will feel the stretch around the shoulders, side and chest.

Repeat on both sides, breathing easily throughout the exercise.

If you find this exercise difficult and you are unable to clasp your fingers together, hold a belt or towel in your upper hand, then reach behind to grasp the belt with your other hand. Gradually inch your hands together as close as possible. As you become more flexible you will find that the belt eventually becomes superfluous.

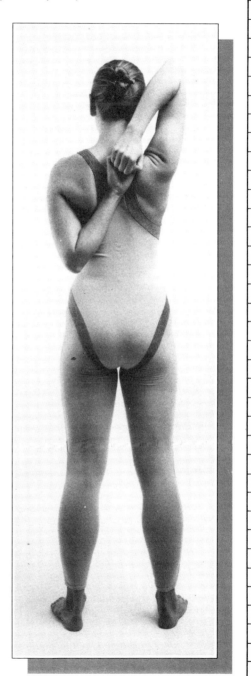

3 Chest stretch

Stand tall with good posture. Place your hands, loosely clasped, on the small of your back. Keeping your spine long and your shoulders down, try and bring your elbows together, holding your furthermost position. You will feel the stretch in your chest.

Breathe easily throughout the exercise.

4 Side stretch

Stand tall with good posture, feet slightly wider than shoulder width. Keeping your spine long and your shoulders down away from your ears, lift up and over to the side as illustrated. Keep your hips stable and facing forwards. Now take one arm over to your side to add extra stretch to the movement.

Hold your furthermost position and avoid the tendency to lean forwards or backwards. Repeat on the other side.

Breathe comfortably throughout the exercise.

5 Spine and trunk twist

Sit upright on the floor with your legs out in front of you. Bend your right leg up towards you, placing the right foot on the outside of your left knee. Keeping your spine long and your shoulders down away from your ears, twist round so that your shoulders face to the side.

Use your left arm as a lever to ease as far round as possible and use your right arm for balance. You will feel the stretch throughout the trunk and spine.

Repeat on both sides, breathing easily throughout the exercise.

6 Seated groin stretch

Sit tall with good posture. Bend your legs up towards you, placing the soles of your feet together and allow your knees to fall towards the floor. Keep your spine long and your shoulders down away from your ears and rest your hands on your calves or ankles. If you find it difficult to sit upright in this position, use your hands behind you for balance. You will feel the stretch along the insides of your thighs and groin.

To increase the stretch, and to stretch the hamstrings at the same time, maintain your long spine position whilst hinging forward from your hips as far as possible, holding your furthermost position.

Having done this, then relax your back, moving towards the floor. You will now feel more stretch in the buttocks and hamstrings. Again, hold your furthermost position.

Breathe easily throughout all of these movements.

7 Lying groin stretch

Lie flat on the floor, pressing your lower back firmly into the ground as you slide both legs up towards your buttocks. Place the soles of your feet together and allow your knees to fall loosely towards the floor. You will feel the stretch along the inner thigh and groin.

Breathe easily throughout the exercise.

8 Lying hamstring stretch

Lie flat on the floor. Slide both feet along the floor until both knees are at an angle of approximately ninety degrees. Make sure that your lower back is firmly pressed into the floor.

Now raise your right leg, grasping it loosely behind the thigh or calf with both hands, yet still keeping your shoulders pressed into the floor. Straighten your leg as fully as possible, then ease it gently as close to your chest as possible. Do not lift your hips off the floor. You will feel the stretch along the back of the leg.

Repeat on both sides, breathing easily throughout the exercise.

9 Standing hamstring stretch

Stand tall with good posture. Bend at the knees and hips until you can easily rest your chest on your thighs. Reach round with your arms and grasp behind your legs, holding your chest and thighs closely together.

From this position, gently try and straighten your legs, whilst still keeping your chest firmly pressed against your thighs. You will feel the stretch along the backs of your legs.

Breathe easily throughout this exercise.

10 Lying quadriceps stretch

Lie face down on the floor, resting your head on your left hand. Press your hips firmly into the floor, bending your right knee up towards your buttocks. Reach round with your right hand to gently ease your right foot closer to your buttocks. You will feel the stretch in the front of your right thigh.

Repeat on both sides, breathing easily throughout.

11 Standing quadriceps stretch

Stand tall with good posture. Holding on to a support, reach behind you with your left arm to loosely grasp your left foot. Ease your foot towards your buttocks whilst keeping your spine long and your bottom tucked under. You will feel the stretch in the front of the left thigh.

Repeat on both sides, breathing easily throughout.

12 Seated hamstring stretch

Sit tall on the floor with legs outstretched. (If this is not possible, bend your knees slightly until your back is straight.) Keeping your spine long and your shoulders down, hinge forwards from the hips, reaching towards your flexed feet with your hands. You will feel the stretch in the backs of your legs and you will also feel the muscles of your back working strongly to maintain your 'long spine' position.

If you are having problems reaching forward, a belt or a towel looped around the feet can help you achieve a greater stretch.

Now relax the back, bringing your chest closer to your thighs, holding your furthermost position.

Breathe easily throughout all the exercises.

13 Standing calf stretch

Stand tall with one leg in front of the other facing a wall or support. Lean forward, placing your hands against the wall at shoulder height. Keep your hips facing forward. Ease your back leg out as far behind you as possible whilst still keeping the heel pressed firmly into the floor. Your spine should be long. You will feel the stretch in the calf of the back leg. Repeat with both legs.

To stretch the calf lower down, adopt the same position, but bend the back knee slightly, still keeping the heel down. Repeat on both sides.

Breathe easily throughout all these movements.

14 Lying hip and thigh stretch

Lie flat on your back with your lower back pressed firmly into the floor. Bring your right knee as close as possible to your chest, holding it there with loosely clasped hands. Keep your other leg firmly stretched out along the floor. You will feel the stretch along the front of the thigh of the outstretched leg and around the hip and buttocks of the bent leg.

Repeat on both sides, breathing easily throughout.

15 Standing hip and thigh stretch

Stand tall with good posture in front of a firm chair or stool. Raise one foot onto the chair back and ease your body slowly towards this foot so that chest and thigh come closer together. Rest your hands loosely on the raised leg and keep your spine long, back leg straight, shoulders down and hips facing forwards. You will feel the stretch along the front of the back leg, and around the hip and buttocks of the bent leg.

Repeat with both legs, breathing easily throughout the exercise.

16 Seated hamstring and groin stretch

Sit tall with good posture with both legs fully outstretched. Bend your right leg so that your right foot rests along your inner thigh with your right knee as close to the floor as possible. Keeping your spine long with shoulders down, hinge forwards from your hips reaching towards your flexed left foot. You will feel the stretch in the back of your left leg and along the groin. You will also feel your back muscles working strongly to maintain your 'long spine' position.

Now relax the back and bring your chest nearer to your thigh, holding your furthermost position.

Breathe easily throughout all these movements.

WORKING WITH A PARTNER

The following few exercises involve a partner. Partners can be very helpful when it comes to increasing one's range of movement. However, partners must work sympathetically and intelligently and not force the exerciser's limbs into any position that might cause injury. The exercises here are passive, in that the partner is doing all the work. The exerciser should try to relax and go with the movement as much as possible.

17 Partner hamstring stretch

Exerciser: lie completely flat on the floor, back pressed firmly into the ground.

Partner: sit to one side of the exerciser as illustrated. Take hold of one of the exerciser's legs at the back of the ankle and the front of the knee as illustrated. Keeping the leg straight gently ease the leg towards the trunk of the exerciser as far as is possible, making sure that the hips do not leave the floor. Hold the furthermost position.

Repeat on the other leg.

18 Partner hip and thigh stretch

Exerciser: lie completely flat on the floor with your back firmly pressed into the ground.

Partner: position yourself to one side of the exerciser as illustrated. Place your left hand on the right thigh of the exerciser and your right hand on his left bent knee. Keep his right leg straight and firmly pressed towards the floor whilst easing his left thigh closer to his chest. Hold the furthermost position.

Repeat on the other leg.

19 Partner groin stretch

Exerciser: lie completely flat on the floor, with your lower back pressed firmly into the ground. Cross your right foot over your left thigh just above the knee.

Partner: Position yourself over the exerciser as illustrated. Place your right hand on the exerciser's left hip and your left hand on the inside of his right knee. Gently apply pressure on both hip and inside knee, easing his right knee closer to the floor. Hold the furthermost position.

20 Partner back stretch

Exerciser: assume a kneeling position as illustrated.

Partner: position yourself above the exerciser as illustrated. Place your left hand on the base of his spine and your right hand in the middle of his back. Lean forward, using your bodyweight to ease his midback and hips down to the floor. Hold the furthermost position.

Appendix 1

PERCEIVED EXERTION

One of the commonly recommended methods for assessing the intensity of one's exercise is to monitor heart rate. However, during weight training, heart rate is not a particularly good indicator of just how hard your body is working, since strong sustained muscular contractions, characteristic of many weight training programmes, tend to lead to higher than normal heart rates.

One way round this problem is to use the feedback from your body at all times. Obvious over-exertion signs have already been mentioned (dizziness, nausea, etc., see page 18), yet the Swedish physiologist Gunnar Borg has shown that most people can quite accurately gauge their exertion intensity using a scale he has devised which he calls his 'Rate of Perceived Exertion' table.

The table is given opposite. As you can see, the scale runs from 6 to 20, and there are also comments to be found alongside the figures. As you are exercising, rate the intensity of the exercise you are doing according to this scale. Warm ups, for instance, will probably fall somewhere between 10 and 12. The heavy strength circuits will probably score around 17. Use this scale to help you get the most from your training. When a training session which used to give a rating of 16 starts to feel like 14, it's probably time to progress.

Borg's Rate of Perceived Exertion Scale

6	No exertion at all
7	Extremely light
8	
9	Very light
10	
11	Light
12	
13	Somewhat hard
14	
15	Hard (heavy)
16	
17	Very hard
18	
19	Extremely hard
20	Maximal exertion

Appendix II

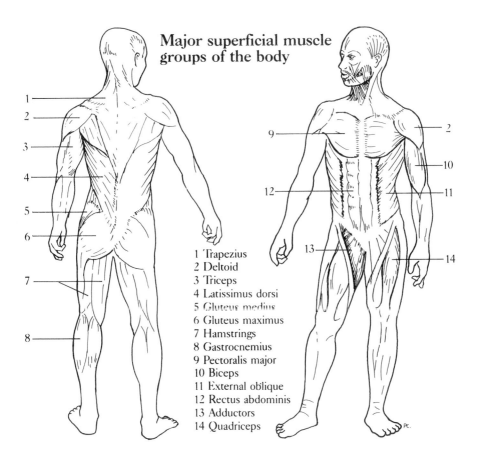

Major superficial muscle
groups of the body

1 Trapezius
2 Deltoid
3 Triceps
4 Latissimus dorsi
5 Gluteus medius
6 Gluteus maximus
7 Hamstrings
8 Gastrocnemius
9 Pectoralis major
10 Biceps
11 External oblique
12 Rectus abdominis
13 Adductors
14 Quadriceps

MUSCLE CHARTS

The following tables may prove useful in
helping you to choose which exercises are
most useful for which muscle group:

WEIGHT TRAINING EXERCISES (LOWER BODY)

Exercise	Muscle groups (major)
Leg press	Gluteals, quadriceps, hamstrings
Front squats	Gluteals, quadriceps, hamstrings
Back squats	Gluteals, quadriceps, hamstrings

(Both front squats and back squats also strengthen the deeper muscles of the back, the erector spinae group)

Squats with dumbbells	Gluteals, quadriceps, hamstrings
Single leg squat	Gluteals, quadriceps, hamstrings, adductors
Lunge	Gluteals, quadriceps, hamstrings, adductors
Step on bench	Gluteals, quadriceps, hamstrings, adductors
Heel raise	Gastrocnemius, soleus (underneath gastrocnemius)
Leg extensions	Quadriceps
Leg curl	Hamstrings, gastrocnemius
Hip extensions	Erector spinae, gluteals, hamstrings
Hyperextensions	Erector spinae, gluteals, hamstrings

WEIGHT TRAINING EXERCISES (UPPER BODY)

Exercise	Muscle groups (major)
Bench press	Pectorals, anterior deltoid, triceps
Press ups	Pectorals, anterior deltoid, triceps
Bench dips	Triceps, pectorals
Dumbbell flyes	Pectorals
Upright rowing	Deltoid, trapezius, biceps
Seated press behind neck	Deltoid, trapezius, triceps
Lateral raise	Deltoid, trapezius
Pull ups	Latissimus dorsi, biceps
Single arm rowing	Latissimus dorsi, biceps
Seated tricep press	Triceps
Arm curl	Biceps
Alternate dumbbell curl	Biceps
Curl up	Rectus abdominis, external oblique
Abdominal crunch	Rectus abdominis, external oblique
Abdominal machine	Rectus abdominis, external oblique

All the plyometric exercises involve virtually all of the muscles of the lower body, to a greater or lesser extent. Beginners may also be surprised at the amount of work that the muscles of the trunk have to do in maintaining the upright position of the body and the position of the pelvis.

STRETCHING EXERCISES

Exercise	Muscle groups (major)
Upper back stretch	Trapezius and the muscle underneath it, the rhomboid, latissimus dorsi
Shoulder stretch	Latissimus dorsi, triceps, pectorals
Chest stretch	Pectorals, anterior deltoid
Side stretch	Latissimus dorsi, external oblique
Spine & trunk twist	Erector spinae, external oblique
Seated groin stretch	Adductors (plus gluteals, hamstrings and erector spinae in positions 2 and 3)
Lying groin stretch	Adductors
Lying hamstring stretch	Hamstrings, gluteals
Standing hamstring stretch	Hamstrings
Lying quadriceps stretch	Quadriceps
Standing quadriceps stretch	Quadriceps
Seated hamstring stretch	Hamstrings (plus erector spinae and gluteals in forward position)
Standing calf stretch	Gastrocnemius (first position) soleus (second position)
Lying hip & thigh stretch	Hamstrings, gluteals
Standing hip & thigh	Hamstrings, gluteals
Seated hamstring & groin	Hamstring, gluteals, adductors (plus erector spinae in forward position)
Partner hamstring stretch	Hamstrings, gluteals
Partner hip & thigh stretch	Hamstrings, gluteals
Partner groin stretch	Adductors
Partner back stretch	Erector spinae

Naturally, these tables over-simplify the story, since other muscles, underneath the superficial muscles (referred to as deep muscles) will also be involved in performing the exercise. Bear in mind, also, that many other muscles not directly involved in an exercise will need to stabilize the rest of the body whilst you are exercising, and some muscles will be acting to prevent undesired movements.

The tables are thus a rough guide only. For more detailed analysis of muscle and movements, the reader is referred to any of the excellent Kinesiology texts on the market.

References

The following references were helpful in putting this guide together:

ARTICLES AND PAPERS

Allen et. al., *Hemodynamic consequences of Circuit Weight Training*, (*Res. Quart.* 47 (3) 299-306, 1976).

Gettman & Pollock, *Circuit Weight Training: a critical review of its benefits*, (*Phys. & Sports Med.* 44-60 9(Jan), 1981).

Gettman et. al., *The effect of Circuit Weight training on strength, cardiovascular function and body composition of adult man*, (*Med. Sci. Sports* Vol 10(3), 1978).

Hempel & Wells, *The cardio-respiratory cost of the Nautilus Express Circuit*, (*Phys. & Sports Med.* Vol 13(4), April 1985).

Hurley et. al., *Effects of high intensity strength training on cardio-vascular function*, (*Med. Sci. Sports* Vol 16(5), 1984).

Morgan & Adamson, *Circuit Training*, (Bell & Sons Ltd., London, 1962).

Wayne, Lee S., *The effects of circuit training using hydraulic resistive exercise on aerobic power, strength & endurance*, (unpublished thesis Univ. Alberta, Canada).

Wilmore et al., *The energy cost of Circuit Weight Training*, (*Med. Sci. Sports* Vol 10(2), 1978).

Wilmore et. al., *Physical alterations consequent to Circuit Weight Training*, (*Med. Sci. Sports* Vol 10(2), 1978).

BOOKS

Harre, D., *Principles of Sports Training*, (SportVerlag, Berlin, 1982).

Fox E.L., & Matthews, D.K., *The Physiological Basis of P.E. and Athletics*, (Saunders, 1976).

Schmolinsky, G., *Track & Field*, (SportVerlag, Berlin, 1982).

Much of the information within this guide was also gathered whilst researching my own previous books. Specifically:
Shape Your Body, Shape Your Life (Thorsons, 1987).
Stretch Into Shape (Thorsons, 1988).

and whilst writing:
The Reebok Guide To Complementary Training For Runners (1987)
and
The Reebok Runner's Log (1988).

Also by the author:

SHAPE YOUR BODY SHAPE YOUR LIFE

The weight training way to total fitness

Tony Lycholat

Weight training — as opposed to weight lifting or body building — is for *you*, for people of any age, shape or build, to help you to shape your life. Benefits — from strength to aerobic fitness — can be gained from using both free and fixed weight systems in an appropriate and progressive manner. Exercise that produces physical change leads to positive mental changes, too, while increased confidence, reduced anxiety and improved self-esteem frequently partner obvious improvements in body shape and fitness. Here the links between mental and physical health are explained in step with a highly practical guide to training with weights: how to exercise, how to choose equipment and devise a programme to suit your requirements are all explained in this lively and fully illustrated passport to a new you!

WEIGHT TRAINING FOR MEN

Tony Lycholat

With the current trends in health and fitness many men are now contemplating training with weights to achieve the positive benefits of exercise, yet for the beginner this is a confusing and difficult task. What exactly are the benefits to be gained from weight training? Which method is best? What is Nautilus equipment? Will I become muscle bound?

This book answers all these questions clearly and simply, with numerous explanatory photographs accompanying the text. It illustrates how to design and implement your personal programme, from warming-up through to cooling down so as to achieve health benefits in safety. This book is invaluable to all those embarking upon a weight training programme for the first time, and it also features many useful ideas for the experienced trainer.

WEIGHT TRAINING FOR WOMEN

Tony Lycholat

With the current trends in health and fitness many women are now contemplating training with weights to achieve the positive benefits of exercise, yet for the beginner this is a confusing and diffcult task. What exactly are the benefits to be gained from weight training? Which method is best? What is Nautilus equipment? Will I become muscle bound? Will I look too masculine?

This book answers all these questions clearly and simply, with numerous explanatory photographs accompanying the text. It illustrates how to design and implement your personal programme, from warming-up through to cooling down so as to achieve health benefits in safety. This book is invaluable to all those embarking upon a weight training programme for the first time, and it also features many useful ideas for the experienced trainer.

STRETCH INTO SHAPE

A fitness improvement programme for all ages

Tony Lycholat

Regular and controlled stretching of muscles and joints offers many positive health benefits. Stretching is appropriate for individuals of any age, size or shape and anyone can begin — and benefit from — this programme at any time. Packed with helpful advice and with easy-to-follow stretching exercises this book will help you to:

★ Improve body posture
★ Increase flexibility and suppleness
★ Ease joint movement
★ Raise athletic performance